Chess: East and West, Past and Present

Chess:

A SELECTION FROM THE
GUSTAVUS A. PFEIFFER
COLLECTION

East and West, Past and Present

Introduction by CHARLES K. WILKINSON, Curator Emeritus
of Near Eastern Art, The Metropolitan Museum of Art

Catalogue by JESSIE McNAB DENNIS, Assistant Curator
of Western European Art, and CHARLES K. WILKINSON

THE METROPOLITAN MUSEUM OF ART, NEW YORK

Distributed by New York Graphic Society, Greenwich, Connecticut

Photographs by Arthur Vitols, except for the following: Cover and Nos. 42, 72, and 73, by William E. Lyall of The Metropolitan Museum of Art; Figures 1–7 and 9 and Nos. 1–8 and 25, by the studios of the Metropolitan; Figure 8, rearranged from Lamm, *Mittelalterliche Gläser*; Nos. 15, 16, and 58, by Wolfgang Hartmann of The Brooklyn Museum; Nos. 27, 33, 35, 38, 41, 43, 51, 56, 62, 76, 81, 84, 85, 90, and 99, by William F. Pons of the Metropolitan; 34, 50, 78, by Walter Yee of the Metropolitan.

Design by Peter Oldenburg. Set in Palatino and Standard. Composition and printing by Connecticut Printers, Inc. Halftone plates by Horan Engraving Co.; color plates by Connecticut Printers. Binding by J. F. Tapley Co.

Contents

Introduction

Chess is a game known by name to almost everyone, and it is played the world over. In Europe and America it is known as an intellectual game with precise rules played with thirty-two pieces on a board of sixty-four squares. Even though players today may be aware that there have been some changes in the rules of the game, most of them are unacquainted with the extent of change in every aspect of chess: the board, the pieces and their names, and the manner of play. Both chess and chessmen display a truly amazing variety. An inquiry into why this is so takes us far afield and back many centuries. Chessmen, even when so crude that they can hardly be called works of art (to use the current meaning of the phrase), reflect a great deal of the time and place in which they were made. This is obviously true in the pieces made in human form, but it is also true in the so-called "conventional" pieces, which, as we shall see, are far more varied than most people are aware. In the representational sets we have almost a miniature world of fashion. They also reflect all sorts of historical events, reminding us especially of wars, both foreign and domestic, and of revolutions and uprisings. Some were made for purposes of propaganda: to further a favorite cause or to express disagreement with international arrangements. Conflicting ideologies, both political and religious, are shown, and even frivolous oppositions are embodied in these small objects, such as that presumed to exist between blondes and brunettes. In fact, all kinds of confrontations are manifest in chessmen, some whimsical, some meaningless, almost all reflecting the artistic fashions of the age in which they were made. They thus form a running commentary on decorative art as it changes from century to century.

The chessmen and boards illustrated in this book range from the seventh century to the present and come from Europe, Asia, Africa, and America. Although all made for a single game, they give a very good idea of the diversity in the world. They form the bulk of an exhibition entitled Chess: East and West, Past and Present, shown at The Brooklyn Museum from April to October, 1968, sponsored by that museum and The Metropolitan Museum of Art. Most of them were given to the Metropolitan by Gustavus A. Pfeiffer, a devoted collector keenly interested in the history and meaning of chess, or purchased from monies bequeathed by him. In addition to the objects acquired directly or indirectly from Mr. Pfeiffer, this publication contains a few ivory chessmen of the early ninth century, excavated at Nishapur by the Metropolitan's Iranian Expedition in 1940, and early Islamic and medieval chessmen given by J. P. Morgan, Alastair Bradley Martin, and others. There is only one piece from the thirteenth century, and none from the fourteenth to the late seventeenth centuries. Pieces of this period are rare in Europe outside of museums and church treasuries, and few have been acquired by American collectors. Within the selection published here, which represents about a third of the Metropolitan's chess collection, much can be learned, by examination and study, of the history of what is probably the world's most fascinating and universal game, and along with it much of the history and interrelation of various parts of the world.

We may have a more thorough understanding of chess and chessmen by inquiring into the origin of the game, the characteristics that distinguish chess from other games, and the meaning of the pieces. Games involving chance and skill in varying proportions have been part of man's life for many thousands of years. In a large group of them, pieces of the same shape or of various shapes are moved on a board with subdivisions, usually square. The invention of such games marks a definite advance in man's progress, inasmuch as they depend on a well-developed sense of order. Some of the games go back to great antiquity. Not only have boards and pieces been preserved from the early Sumerian and Egyptian civilizations, but also pictures of such games being played. A wall painting in the Tombs of the Queens in Upper Egypt shows Queen Nefertari (the queen of Ramesses II, reigned 1304–1237 B.C.) playing a board game (*senet*), and an Egyptian papyrus of about 1000 B.C. shows a seated gazelle and a lion engaged in the same pastime.

Although games of this type are usually called board games, the term is not entirely satisfactory, as they need not be, and often are not, played on boards. Any marked surface will do. Chess is no exception in this respect. Chess was and is often played on a piece of leather or a marked cloth. Apart from the matter of material, there are many variations of the "board." It need not be square, or even rectangular: circular chess has been known for centuries. The board may have sixty-four squares (the board with which we are familiar), but it can as easily have 100, 110, 144, or an even greater number. In fact, what with recent developments, the "board" need not even be of two dimensions, for 1908 saw the introduction of three-dimensional "space chess." But before going into such details it would be well to identify the game itself.

Chess is a game of war played on a marked surface between symbolic armies of a certain composition, usually, but not always, two in number. Although there are other games of a warlike nature, with pieces being besieged or captured, in chess the opposing sides represent the four main branches of a military force once used in a certain part of the ancient world: chariotry, elephant corps, cavalry, and infantry. It was an army of this kind that Alexander the Great encountered when he invaded northwest India in 326 B.C. Originally in chess each army had, in addition to these four branches, a king and a counselor or minister. Pieces were captured; pieces could be promoted. The game came to an end by checkmate (when a king, rendered vulnerable, was unable to move or screen himself), by stalemate (when the side whose turn it was to move could not do so), or by bare king (when a king was the sole survivor of one side).

Despite the changes the game has undergone, with the loss of many of its original symbolic meanings, a continuity can be established. There was variety even in the early days of chess, and there is today. The invention of new forms has never ceased. Many players in the Western world, among them the famous champion Capablanca, have devised new forms of the game, adding new pieces with particular moves, but most of these innovations have died out after a short while. One example, included here (No. 50), is a set that has a board nine squares by thirteen, the major pieces of one side fronted by a double row of pawns. This invention of François Gilot, a nineteenth-century watchmaker, was inspired by the Crimean War, and the major pieces portray the leading military and political figures in that conflict.

Just as there have been changes in the form of the game, there have been changes in the freedom of choice in making the moves. In ancient times dice were used, which limited that freedom; today computers have come into the game, and human beings have become merely onlookers, or rather, the outcome of the game depends on the preliminary instruction of the machine, which of course is still arranged by human beings. So far this form of chess has been played with no regard to restriction of the time allotted to each opponent. Until a restriction is made—and until the quality of the play improves—such games can hardly attain championship level.

The history of chess is by no means simple, and the origin of the game, like the origin of most ideas, is neither a clear nor a precisely dated event. Nevertheless, a good deal is known about it as a result of research in ancient literature, study of the ancient and modern names of the pieces, and consideration of the game itself as played in various parts of the world. The inquiry has been especially well done, with a most careful balancing of the evidence, by H. J. R. Murray, whose book *The History of Chess*, published in 1913, is still the authoritative work on the subject.

Chess has no such great antiquity as the board games played in ancient Egypt and Mesopotamia. Although, as stated above, the army represented on the chessboard existed at the time of Alexander the Great, there is no reason, despite medieval European association of his name with the game, to believe that the essential game existed even in his day. However, a game that is recognizably chess was being played in India by the sixth or seventh century of our era. The four branches of the army were named in Sanskrit *chatur anga* (four members), and the word *chaturanga* passed into Persia during the Sasanian period (A.D. 226–637), where it became *chatrang*. Chariotry had by this time been abandoned in actual armies, but the concept endured on the board.

There are two references to chess in Persian literature of the Sasanian period, one minor and one major. The date of their composition is uncertain. In one, the *Karnamak-i-Artakhshatr-i-Papakan* (considered by E. G. Browne to have been composed about 600, though no manuscript of that date exists), chess is one of the accomplishments in which Ardeshir, the first Sasanian king (226–241), became skilled. In the other work, the *Chatrang-namak* (Book of Chess), the story is told that an Indian king, called Dewarsam, had a chess set sent to the Persian shahinshah Khusrau-i-Anushakruban (Khusrau I, 531–538) with the threat that, if the shah could not solve the game, he would have to pay the customary tribute instead of receiving it. The set was a magnificent one, with one side of emeralds, the other of rubies (still the usual opposing colors in Indian chess). A Persian, Wajurmitr, after delaying several days "to prove he was the wisest in the land," came to the assistance of the shah, and declared that *chatrang* was a war game, correctly identified the pieces, and proceeded to beat the Indian envoy in a dozen games. Wajurmitr then devised another game, with thirty white pieces and thirty black, which was played with dice, called *neu-artakshir* (probably backgammon), and then went to India and faced the Indians with the problem of interpreting his game. They failed to do so, and, as a result, paid twice the normal tribute. It is to be noticed that in this story dice are not mentioned, although they were used in chess at an early date. This tale is one of several instances in which the Persians, although they obviously considered themselves superior in every way, were ready to credit the invention of the game to India.

Although the conquest of Persia was accomplished by the Arab armies about A.D. 638, there was a great revival of Persian literature in the tenth century, and by the beginning of the eleventh century Firdausi had finished Persia's great epic poem, the *Shahnama*, which relates the deeds and accomplishments of Persia's ancient kings and heroes. In this poem there are two long stories about chess, of which the second deals with the invention of the game. Firdausi relates that chess was invented as a means of breaking to the mother of Gav, an Indian king, the news of the loss of another of her sons, Talhand, in a battle with his brother. The tragedy was enacted in miniature on the board, after which the bereaved woman, racked with anguish, neither ate nor drank but spent the remainder of her life playing chess. The story has points of interest apart from its crediting India with the invention of chess. We learn that the game was played on a board of a hundred squares. The men were of teak and ivory, a natural choice of materials in India. The composition of the armies and the arrangement of the pieces is given. Next to the shah stood his adviser. Each was flanked by an elephant, and they in turn were flanked by camels, who are declared in the text to be "men of good intentions." Next to them were horses with cavaliers, and finally valiant *rukhs* (charioteers or heroes) with "lips full of blood and foam." In front of these pieces were the *piyadeh* (infantrymen). The moves of the pieces were mostly more restricted than they are now, but it is to be noted that the horse's move was of three squares of which one was to one side of his path— the knight's move of the present time.

Decimal chess is one of several forms mentioned by early Islamic writers. Another was "Great Chess," of which one form was played on a board with eleven squares by ten, and this became known as Timur's chess. With the death of Timur (Tamerlane) in 1405 the game seems to have died out, though another form of "Great Chess," with a board thirteen squares by thirteen, was used in the nineteenth century in Turkey.

The other chess story told by Firdausi in the *Shahnama* is related to that in the *Chatrang-namak* and, like it, speaks of an envoy sent from India to Persia, though in this case with a message written on silk. The purport, however, was the same: unless the Persians could name the pieces and work out the moves of chess, no tribute would be paid. The Persians were saved from

1. Buzurjmihr explaining the moves of chess to the Indian envoy in the presence of Shah Nushirwan, from a xiv-century *Shahnama*. Joseph Pulitzer Bequest Fund, 34.24.1

this disgrace by Buzurjmihr, the Persian counselor of Nushirwan (Khusrau I), who explained the moves to the envoy in the presence of the shah in "the palace which seemed all throne, and the throne all shah." No paintings of this scene contemporary with Firdausi have survived, but there are examples from the fourteenth century onward, of which two are in the Metropolitan. In one (Figure 1) the board, although squared, is not checkered, though in a miniature of the same scene in a fifteenth-century *Shahnama* in Tehran, the board is squared and checkered and, in addition, each square is decorated. The story in the *Shahnama*, like its Sasanian predecessor, ends with the return match, so to speak, with the Persian sage inventing *nard* (backgammon) and taking it to the rajah in India, where no one is able to explain its meaning. This scene is also depicted in the Metropolitan's fourteenth-century manuscript, with Buzurjmihr seated on the ground before the rajah and his court (Figure 2). It will be seen that the *nard* board is marked in an entirely different way from the chessboard and that the pieces upon it are differently disposed.

It is not without interest that a seventh-century wall painting, now in the Hermitage Museum, discovered a few years ago in Pianjikent, to the southeast of Tashkent (M. Bussagli, *Painting in Central Asia*, Geneva, 1963, p. 46), shows a board very similar to that in Figure 2. Several paintings at Pianjikent seem to be associable with the *Shahnama*, and it is possible that this particular one, even though painted four centuries earlier than Firdausi's masterpiece was written, deals with the same traditions.

The idea in Persia that chess was inferior to backgammon, indicated clearly in these stories, is emphasized in various miniature paintings that have survived. It is especially well shown in one from the early fifteenth century, now in the Berenson Collection at I Tatti. In this, both games are depicted: the grandees in magnificent garments seated on a rug play backgammon, while men of lower rank play chess beneath them on the paved floor.

The Arabs, who were victorious over the Persians in the first half of the seventh century, did not have quite the same ideas. Ya'qubi, who lived in the tenth century, states that after the invention of backgammon for a certain Indian king (the invention of an Indian, not a Persian as in the Persian stories), chess was invented for a later king, Balhait, because the qualities that it inspired were esteemed above those of backgammon. For chess one needed prudence and knowledge, whereas backgammon, which was played with dice, encouraged the acceptance of chance and fate. In Ya'qubi's story two Persian concepts are reversed: firstly, in the assertion that chess is superior to backgammon, and, secondly, that it was invented later. Ya'qubi agrees with the Persians that chess originated in India.

2. Buzurjmihr showing the game of backgammon to the Indian rajah, from a xiv-century *Shahnama*. Joseph Pulitzer Bequest Fund, 34.24.2

Ma'sudi, another Arab writer of the tenth century, has a somewhat similar tale, in which the king, on seeing the game of chess, immediately became interested in it (although, in this instance, it was not invented especially for him). Ma'sudi gives many details of the game as it was played in India and elsewhere. He tells of the uses of chess: for studying the strategy of war, and as an allegory of the celestial spheres. Furthermore, he says, the board served for making mathematical calculations. Some of Ma'sudi's details sound far-fetched, for example, that the chief use of ivory in India was for the manufacture of chess and backgammon pieces. He also tells us that the Hindus played for high stakes, for stuffs and jewels, not even stopping at the proverbial shirt: "When they play they have near them a caldron of reddish ointment and the players wager fingers, forearm, elbow and other parts of their body, cauterizing the wound with this ointment, which is peculiar to India and extraordinarily effective. The custom of which I speak is a notorious fact." It is interesting to note that in Persia the expression *dast-i-Khun* (the hand of blood) is used for the last move at chess or for any game in which a player figuratively stakes his limbs.

Ibn Khallikan, the thirteenth-century author of a remarkable biographical dictionary that incorporates much information of earlier texts, writing of as-Suli, probably the greatest chess master of the tenth century, states that the game was invented by Sissa ibn Dahir, of Hindustan, for the amusement of King Shihram.

The whole matter is perhaps most concisely and sensibly stated by al-'Adli, an Arab chess master of the ninth century, who wrote much about the game. Speaking of a kind of chess, he says, as quoted by Murray: "And this form is the form of chess which the Persians took from the Indians and which we took from the Persians."

In Oriental literature the invention of chess was closely associated with kings. This association exists in European stories of the invention of chess also, which, while losing none of the fancifulness of the Eastern tales, somehow or other drop out India as the birthplace of the game. One of the best-known examples is a sermon, written in Latin in the thirteenth century by a Dominican monk, Jacobus de Cessolis. It became extremely popular and was translated into many languages; William Caxton first printed it in English in 1474. In the first part of this sermon the invention of chess is described. According to Cessolis, this occurred in Babylon, in the land of the Chaldees, where reigned (in Caxton's version) the son of "Nabugodonosor," a king named "Evyl Merodach" (actually, the son of Nebuchadnezzar was named

Amel-Marduk; he reigned from 604 to 561 B.C.), "a jolye man without jus-tyce, and so euel that he did do hewe his faders body in thre hondred pieces," and gave these pieces to the birds. At the behest of his subjects, a philosopher named Exerses (apparently a corruption of Xerxes), known also by the Greek name Philometor, invented chess to keep the wicked king from idleness and to satisfy his desire for novelty. It was pointed out to him that in the game "the glorie of the people is the dygnyte of the kyng." In actuality, the effects of the invention were negligible for, according to more accurate records, Amel-Marduk, who was restrained by neither law nor decency, was assassi-nated by a priestly opposition after he had reigned less than three years.

Sparked by this reference to the Babylonian king, the Assyriologist C. J. Gadd has made the suggestion that chess was of Babylonian origin, offering ingenious interpretations of a cuneiform tablet found in Erech to support it. He suggests that there is a connection with the use of a "river," such as ap-pears on Chinese chessboards, and the "line of the river" in the text of the tablet, and also draws attention to the fact that the early Islamic rook (see No. 2) is very similar in shape to the front of the Sumerian chariot of the third millennium B.C. The suggestion that chess was really a Babylonian in-vention would seem, however, to require more substantial evidence than has so far been presented.

Cessolis, like many medieval writers, made historical characters responsi-ble for much with which they had nothing to do. Having given his opinion that chess was invented to cure the king of Babylonia of his evil ways, he went on to say that the game was taken to Egypt by Alexander the Great. It is just possible that the Persians, if not the Greeks, introduced chess into Egypt, because the Sasanian king Khusrau II invaded Egypt and ruled it from 619 to 628. But whether chess was brought into Egypt by the Persians or a decade later by the Arabs after they had destroyed the Persian Empire, it was under Arab rule that the game really spread there. By the eighth century the Arabs were in control of much of northern Africa and western Europe, and by the ninth their authority was firmly established. This great military success brought in its train many cultural advantages, for at this time Islam was a potent revivifying force with much tolerance for other religions, provided tribute was duly paid or, in the case of individuals, a tax was paid in lieu of military service.

In the early days of Islam the game of chess was much developed, as we know from the writings of as-Suli and al-'Adli among others. Among the Muslims, as opposed to the Indians and Persians, it was played in the very highest circles. We read, for example, of ar-Razi, a rival of al-'Adli, playing against him in the presence of al-Mutawakkil, an Abbasid caliph (847–862). This is interesting, for al-Mutawakkil was much more orthodox in his opinions than many other caliphs, and chess, probably because of its connection with gambling, was not acceptable to many religious authorities.

Politically minded rulers of the Islamic world seem sometimes to have steered a middle course. Kai Kaus ibn Iskander, the eleventh-century ruler of Gurgan in north Persia, in his book of precepts written for his son, the *Qabus Nama* (*A Mirror for Princes*), says: "Do not make a habit of constantly playing backgammon and chess, and never for a stake, unless it be for a fowl, or a dinner, or the like. . . . Playing without money is training for the mind, but for gold and silver is gambling."

The Arabs quickly taught the Christians and Jews. At first they all played the game according to the Arab rules. Many chess problems of this period survived and were incorporated into Christian manuscripts, of which one of the most famous was written in 1283 for Alfonso X (Alfonso the Wise). The manuscript is now in the library of the Monastery of San Lorenzo del Escorial, near Madrid. The first part is full of pictures of chess problems, most of which are Muslim. In another part there are variations of chess, such as decimal chess with ten squares a side, and one form of "Great Chess" with twelve squares a side, a game here credited to India, and indicated as played with or without dice. Another variation included is four-handed chess, a game which, with some differences, was described by al-Biruni, the author of a famous work on India, as having been played in the early eleventh century. Yet another version is described, astronomical chess, played on a circular board. (Round chess is also mentioned by Arab writers, attributed by them to both India and Byzantium.)

The problems in the Alfonso manuscript are shown in such a way that there is much supplementary information. They are displayed on a checkered chessboard between two players, often with onlookers. The opponents and onlookers can easily be distinguished by their dress as Christians or Muslims (Figure 3). Even the actual making of chessmen and how the pieces were stored on shelves are shown in the book.

We do not know how extensive the checkering of the chessboard was in Europe at this time. A thirteenth-century Florentine manuscript of the *Bonus Socius*, a collection of chess problems compiled in the twelfth century in Lombardy, shows boards that are divided into squares but not checkered. The names of the pieces in the text and in the diagrams do not always cor-

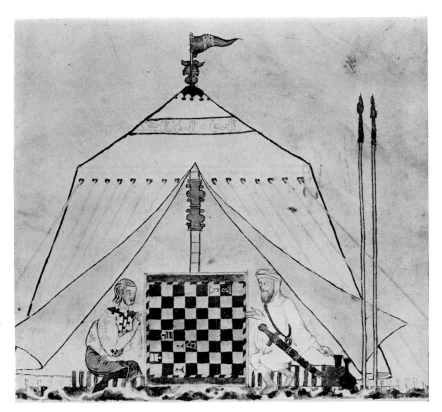

3. A Christian and a Muslim playing chess, from the chess manuscript of Alfonso the Wise, 1283.

respond; for example, the queen is called *regina* in the text but *ferz* in the diagram, from the Arabicized word *firzan*, counselor. This discrepancy suggests that the diagrams, including, of course, the boards, were copied without change from older manuscripts, both names being understood. A similar situation exists in English in regard to "rook" (from the Persian *rukh*) and "castle," the latter word denoting the same piece in the change of positions known as "castling."

Having reached Europe and quickly spread over the whole of it, chess assumed an important role, and there are many references to the game in medieval literature quite apart from those dealing with the problems of the game. Chess-playing scenes are by no means rare in works of art such as

4. Four scenes of
courtship. Ivory panel,
XIV century. Gift of
Ann Payne Blumenthal,
38.108

OPPOSITE:
5. Detail of The
Chess Players, by
Francesco di Giorgio,
XV century. Bequest of
Maitland Fuller Griggs,
43.98.8

ivory boxes, tapestries, and paintings. Chess is referred to in many romance
ballads and poems. Knights as well as ladies played this game, and both
turned their knowledge of it, with its social opportunities and the close prox-
imity it entailed, to advantage. Tristan and Isolde, for example, played chess
on the ship that was bringing Isolde to King Mark—a detail that Wagner
omitted. On an ivory panel belonging to the Metropolitan, a chess game is
one of four scenes of courtship (Figure 4). Chess plays a great part in a medieval *chanson de geste* relating the noble deeds of Huon of Bordeaux, written about 1200 and translated into English by Lord Berners in 1534. In this
story there is a game between a Muslim and a Christian, between a young

lady, the daughter of a king named Yvorin, and Huon. The lady is an expert, and her father would have Huon play with her, Huon having boasted of his prowess in the game. If Huon loses, he will lose his head; if he wins, he may bed with the king's daughter for a night. Huon asks, "What game will you play, by moves, or with dice?"—a reminder that two forms were used in many parts of the world. "Let it be with moves," says the lady. Having fallen in love with Huon, despite the fact that he is disguised as a varlet, she easily manages to lose. Huon, from a sense of chivalry, did not accept his prize, and the lady, in Berners' translation, went away muttering, "A false faynted heart, Muhammed confound thee, for if I had known that thou wouldst thus have refused my company, I would have mated thee and then thou wouldst hadst lost thy head." The subject of men playing chess against women is not peculiar to Europe, but appears also in Oriental stories. In the East as in Europe, young women seemed to prefer to trust to their skill rather than risk the chance imposed by dice. A painting by Francesco di Giorgio (Figure 5)

could well portray such a scene as that related in the story of Huon. The matter of playing chess for a woman goes back in Europe at least to the eleventh century, for we learn that Mathilda, daughter of Otto II, was "won" as a result of a chess match between Ezzo, the Count Palatine, and her brother Otto III—a matter which, whether it pleased the lady or not, could hardly have pleased the clergy.

Just as chess was not pleasing to many straitlaced Muslims, so too it was by no means approved of by the Church in Christendom—especially the Greek Orthodox Church in the Byzantine Empire. Cardinal Damianus (1007–1072), bishop of Ostia, wrote to reprove a bishop for sporting away his evenings with the vanity of chess and so defiling with the pollution of a sacrilegious game the hand that offered up the body of the Lord. A most intemperate remark, for a hand performs of necessity many lowly functions.

But despite attacks of this nature, the monk Cessolis edifies by means of

6. Woodcut from the title page of Jacobus de Cessolis, *Libro di giuocho di scacchi*, printed by Antonio Miscomini in Florence, 1493–1494. Harris Brisbane Dick Fund, 43.37

the game. His Latin sermon was entitled in its Italian translation *Libro di giuocho di scacchi . . . deglhuomini & degli offitii denobili.* It was printed by, among others, Antonio Miscomini, in Florence in 1493–1494, with woodcut illustrations (Figures 6 and 7). The work was well known in England, for after Caxton's first edition in Bruges in 1474, he printed another in London, this time with illustrations, unfortunately much inferior in quality to those printed by Miscomini. Caxton's translation, from a French version, is called *The Game and Pley of the Chesse.*

The sermon deals with all sorts and conditions of men, allegorically represented in their various ranks by chessmen. It is the use of chessmen that distinguishes it from some earlier moralities. That the work was popular is not altogether surprising, as chess was played by many people who would understand its metaphorical meanings. Cessolis divided European society into two major parts, the nobility and the commoners, represented by the major pieces and the pawns. Of the major chessmen, the king and knights are symbols of obvious rank, and the queen is representative of her sex in general—concerning which Cessolis has some very salty stories. There remain two important pieces—the bishop, usually known then in Europe as the *alfin* or *auphin*, derived from the Arabic *al fil* (the elephant), and the rook—to which no single definite meaning was attached. Cessolis makes the former represent judges, whose duty it was to counsel the king and to give sentence well and justly, and the latter the king's legatees, vicars, or deputies. It is noteworthy that despite the author's being a monk the Church is not represented. Each of the pawns is related to the piece before whom he stands, and it is surprising how many professions or occupations are touched on. Each piece is given due attention, and each man is warned against the moral disease peculiar to his occupation. The whole concept is typical of Christian Europe. The author is much concerned with the relationship between master and man and in Caxton's version says, "we see nowadays many fools who deign not to use the gross meats of the commoners and flee the coarse clothing and manners of a servant. Every wise man a servant that truly serveth his master is free and not bonde; but a foole that is ouerproude is bonde." Cessolis makes it clear that an armorer could not become a knight, nor a servant a master. It is the same aspect of the Western world embodied in a verse of a well-known nineteenth-century hymn, a verse conscientiously omitted by present-day clergymen:

> *The rich man in his castle,*
> *The poor man at his gate,*
> *God made them high or lowly*
> *And ordered their estate.*

Although chess flourished in both Islam and Christendom, allegorical interpretations such as this would have been impossible in Islam. Where Christendom and Islam could meet is in the allegory of Death making the final move. Emphasis in Europe was often laid on the fact that the bigger the piece, the lower it sank into the bag—a matter of consolation perhaps to the great majority in a rigidly defined society. Though this particular emphasis is lacking in the East, Omar Khayyám could write, as paraphrased by Fitzgerald:

> *'Tis all a Chequer-board of Nights and Days*
> *Where Destiny with Men for Pieces plays:*
> *Hither and thither moves, and mates and slays,*
> *And one by one back in the closet lays.*

In the development of chess in Europe, Russia for many centuries did not follow the general pattern, but nonetheless was highly influenced by the Muslim world in a very direct way. This is hardly surprising in view of the fact that there was much trade among Mesopotamia, Persia, and Russia, mostly by river routes such as the Dnieper and Volga, as has been demonstrated by finds of coins and other artifacts. Such trade reached even remote Scandinavia, where Muslim glass of the ninth or tenth century has been preserved. The name for chess that was used in Russia was taken from the Persian, and there is another close bond in that the original elephant remained such in Russia. The elephants on one side were usually distinguished from those on the other by having a mahout, the man who controls the elephant with his pointed goad, seated on the animal's head. This curious distinction is sometimes found in Oriental sets when the color is the same on both sides. Another notable difference, but not due to Islamic influence, between Russian sets and those of the rest of Europe is in the rooks, which are represented as boats. This peculiarity is also to be observed in Siam, Annam, Cambodia, and Java, and in Bengal, where it would seem that, according to Murray, the old Persian word *rukh*, adopted but not understood by the Muslims, was identified with the Sanskrit word *roka*, boat. Later, the piece was called in vernacular Bengali *nauka*, boat.

Muslim influence also extended eastward and affected India. That India should be affected despite its being the birthplace of chess is by no means surprising, for certain parts of that subcontinent fell under the sway of Islam and have remained so to this day. Some of the changes, however, are not attributable to this alone, and in certain parts of India, such as the Deccan and middle India, sets are used in which the elephant, instead of being next to the king and his minister, where the American and English bishop stands, is placed in the corner, dispossessing the rook. A camel is in the place next to the king (see Nos. 13 and 18).

There was trade between the Islamic world and the Far East, but there is little evidence of it in the appearance of Far Eastern chessboards and men. They are very different from those of both Muslim countries and India, to such an extent that many have questioned whether the game played in the Orient is truly chess, and whether it derived from India or was born in the Orient. In China, the board is divided by a gap between the two sides known as the "river," and the pieces are put on the intersections and not within the rectangles (No. 25). The men themselves are circular disks with their names written upon them, red for one side and blue for the other. (The elaborate ivory Chinese chessmen carved for the American and European market must here be left aside, as they were made for export.) Despite all these differences, there are ties both to the original game and to that played in other lands. The names of the Chinese pieces show the underlying relationship. The pieces represent the general, counselor, elephant, assistant, horse, chariot, cannon or catapult, and foot soldiers.

In Korea, the game somewhat resembles Chinese chess, but the "river" between the sides is abandoned. The board is divided into a rectangular network of eight units by nine. The names, however, are similar in meaning to those in China and again are inscribed on flat pieces. In Japan the board is divided into eighty-one oblongs (nine by nine) upon which the flat pieces are placed (No. 34). The names are far more elaborate (not to say precious) than those of the Chinese men, such as jeweled, gold, and silver generals, and the honorable horse—which, it is important to note, makes the same peculiar move as the knight, a move that seems to be universal in chess. There are also a flying chariot and foot soldiers.

The name of the game itself and the names of the pieces, occasionally mentioned in the course of this essay, have undergone many changes during the passage of time and their journeyings into distant parts of the world. A study of these changes is most interesting, but it is also complicated, requiring much philological knowledge. Furthermore, it presents many points that are obscure and debatable. A number of scholars have worked on such problems, many from a limited and special point of view, but some have considered the nomenclature of chess in its entirety. Once again, the most judicious summing up of this knowledge is to be found in Murray's *History of Chess.*

Some versions of the name of the game itself have derived from the original Sanskrit name, *chaturanga,* as is the case in Spain, but in most countries in Europe the word has been based on the Persian name of the largest piece, the *shah* (king). Some of the derivations are shown here, reflecting the principal lines of development:

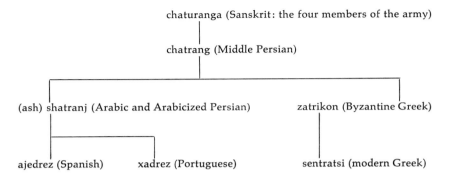

chaturanga (Sanskrit: the four members of the army)

chatrang (Middle Persian)

(ash) shatranj (Arabic and Arabicized Persian)   zatrikon (Byzantine Greek)

ajedrez (Spanish)   xadrez (Portuguese)   sentratsi (modern Greek)

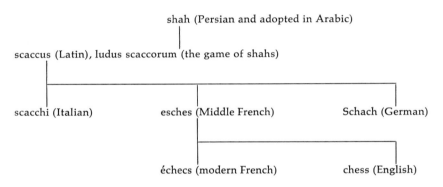

shah (Persian and adopted in Arabic)

scaccus (Latin), ludus scaccorum (the game of shahs)

scacchi (Italian)   esches (Middle French)   Schach (German)

échecs (modern French)   chess (English)

In one instance, in Russian, the word for chess (*shahmaté* and the modern expression *shakhmatnoy egry*) derived not from the simple word *shah* but from *shah mat* (checkmate), which in Persian means "the king is at a loss," not, as is sometimes thought, "the king is dead"—the king does not die in chess. The error is due to the confusion of the Arabic word *mat* (dead) with the Persian *mat*.

Some of these old European forms have supplied us with words now in everyday use whose origin in the game of chess has been forgotten. Among these is the word "exchequer," from the Middle English "escheker," a chessboard, the checkered board having been used as a form of abacus in Norman times. From this, in turn, we get the English "cheque" and the American "check."

The association of the chessboard with numbers has a long history. Al-

'Adli speaks of a board in which the squares have values from one to one of ten million, on which counters or small stones could be piled as required (Murray, *History of Chess*, ill. p. 338). Ya'qubi, in his version of the Indian queen having the loss of her son explained to her through chess, relates how she wished to reward Qaflan, the philosopher who invented the game for her. One grain of corn was put on the first square of the board, two on the second, double that on the next, and so on, the geometrical progression reaching a tremendous sum. Although not directly connected with chess, this association of numerals with India was of importance to the Arabs and to the West in the introduction of the so-called "Arabic" numerals, which included the all-important zero, acknowledged as having come from India.

As chess went from land to land, the names of the men went also, losing their meaning except as identification of the pieces. An instance of this is the English word "rook." The word is the old Persian word *rukh* corruptly pronounced, which reached England by way of the Arabic *rukhkh* and was turned into the Latin *roccus*. It is to be noted that the piece itself was not confused with the bird called a rook. Confusions of this sort could occur, and one theory of the introduction of the word "castle," used to denote the same piece, is by confusion of the Italian *rocco*, the chess piece, with *rocca*, a rock or fortress. As we have seen above, a somewhat similar process took place in Bengal in connection with the same piece, resulting in a boat's representing what had originally been a chariot.

Some of the changes were probably the result of writing on chess, of which there was much in Europe. As an example, M. A. H. Vida, the bishop of Alba, composed a poem in Latin in the first part of the sixteenth century, describing in it a chess game between Apollo and Mercury before the other gods. Centaurs and archers take the place of bishops, fitting well into his classical scheme, and Vida also introduced from classical sources the elephant with a tower or castle on his back, which he employed for the rook; the Persian *rukh*, of course, was meaningless to him. Some of these literary substitutions led to changes in the shaping of the pieces, especially after the sixteenth century. Another influence on the names of the pieces were the moralities, Cessolis' work among them.

For several centuries the names transmitted from the Persians by the Muslims persisted in one form or another. The Persian *farzin* thus became *firzan* in Arabic, which with its definite article *"al"* became *aferez* in Spanish, and *fers* or *ferz* in a number of countries. The Persian *pil* (elephant) became *(al) fil* in Arabic, and gave rise to a number of corruptions in Europe, where the association of the piece with an elephant was lost: *alphyn, alfinus, auphin,* and even *delfinus* or *dauphin*. Other names were used as well as those of Persian origin, as is obvious from figural pieces that have survived from the twelfth century. Instead of *fers* we have a queen, the Latin *regina* or *domina* translated or transmuted into a number of languages. The elephant became all sorts of things: a sage or an old man in England, Germany, and Sweden, a bishop in England, France, and Germany, a count (Germany), a fool (France and Germany), or an archer, standard-bearer, or runner (Germany). The Persian *asp* (horse) was translated rather than adopted by the Arabs and became *faras*, the steed alone representing the cavalry. In Europe in medieval times the horse became a knight, as suited the age of chivalry; only in Spain is it still called a horse. In modern Germany the name of the piece has changed to indicate the kind of move it makes: it is called *Springer* (jumper). It will be noticed that the older names keep more closely to the original meaning of the game whereas the more modern ones, which were encouraged by the particular kind of moral and literary life of Europe, have obscured that meaning.

A comprehensive study of the shapes of chessmen cannot be undertaken here. In fact, such a study would be extremely difficult even if quantities of illustrative material were included, for there are many gaps in our knowledge. Yet, when one looks at any considerable number of chess sets, whether from the East or the West, what immediately strikes one is that they fall into two main groups. In one, the pieces embody the names they bear. The king is a miniature royal figure, the elephant is an elephant, the pawn a little foot soldier. In the other group, the pieces are distinctive arbitrary forms, recognizable to the players who use them but meaningless to those unaccustomed to them. Such are usually termed "conventional" sets, a rather unsatisfactory term in that there are so many conventions. There is some reason to believe that both types of chessmen have been used from the game's earliest days. Unfortunately, our knowledge of chess pieces before the Islamic era is almost nonexistent. There is a small stone elephant of the Sasanian period in the Metropolitan Museum (No. 1) that may well have been a chess piece, but it cannot be proven such.

The earliest pieces that are surely chessmen and can be definitely dated (from the early ninth century at the latest) are those that were excavated by the Metropolitan's Iranian Expedition at Nishapur in northeast Persia (No. 2). These are of ivory, one side being left white, the other stained green, contrasting colors popular in Asia to the present day. The pieces are interesting for several reasons, not entirely for their great age. Most of them may be considered nonrepresentational, but at least two are clearly animals. The horse is easy to recognize. The other, an elephant, is less so, but has the general silhouette fairly well delineated. The tusks, however, have become rather hornlike, a misplacement that was much exaggerated in later pieces. The *rukh* with its V-cut in the top and vertical lines in the front and back may represent a chariot, though in a very stylized form. The *shah* and his *firzan* are represented by pieces that have been considered thrones, or they may be very roughly blocked seated human figures. It is even possible, judging by early representational pieces, to consider them blocked-out figures of personages riding on elephants, treated in the most stylized and simple way; the small scale does not make this apparent at first glance. The pawns are small pyramids. The pieces may well have been made in a not entirely realistic manner so that they would be easy to handle in playing. Incidentally, it is wise not to put too much stress on the nonrepresentational character of Muslim pieces, for the taboo on representation in things that were not strictly of a religious nature was not particularly strong, especially in Persia with its never dying pictorial tradition.

In Osnabrück, Germany, is a crystal set, long associated with Charlemagne (emperor 800–814), who traditionally has been thought to have received chessmen from the caliph Harun ar-Rashid. Recent scholarship has considered the set to be much later, even possibly from the thirteenth century. The association with Charlemagne, however, cannot be deemed mythical on the grounds that the shape of the chessmen did not exist so early, for the closeness to the pieces excavated at Nishapur is remarkable and would seem to indicate that such a late date cannot be upheld. Another set made of crystal, however, known as the Ager chessmen, which belonged to one of the counts of Urgel, has decoration that is surely of the eleventh century (Figure 8).

A few early representational pieces from the Near and Middle East, made in the centuries immediately following the conquest of Persia by the Arab armies, have survived. Among them is a knight mounted on a horse, carved in ivory, found in Samarkand and dated by J. Orbeli to the eighth or ninth century. The only other chess piece composed of realistic human and animal forms that has been given such an early date is an outstanding one for many reasons. Some have doubted its being a chessman because of its size—it is over six inches high—and its great elaboration. It, too, is said to have belonged to Charlemagne. It comes from the Treasury of St. Denis, but it has nothing to do with yet another group of so-called "Charlemagne" pieces in the same collection, now in the Cluny Museum, Paris, which are certainly of later date.

If this truly is a chess piece, and it probably is, it is the most magnificent of all. It consists of an elephant with a man seated on a howdah, which is decorated at the back with soldiers with drawn swords. The elephant is surrounded by horsemen, one of whom, smaller than the rest, has been encircled by the elephant's trunk and lifted from his saddle. A naked man hangs head down on the elephant's forehead. On the base of the piece is an inscription in Kufic script of a style not incongruous with the early date some have ascribed to it. This gives the name of the maker, Yusef al-Bahili. Ernst Kühnel suggests that the name indicates he came from near Basra at the head of the Persian Gulf, an important city in the eighth and ninth centuries. It is

8. Crystal chessmen willed to the church in Ager, Catalonia, by Ermengand I, Count of Urgel, in 1010. Collection of the Countess of Béhague

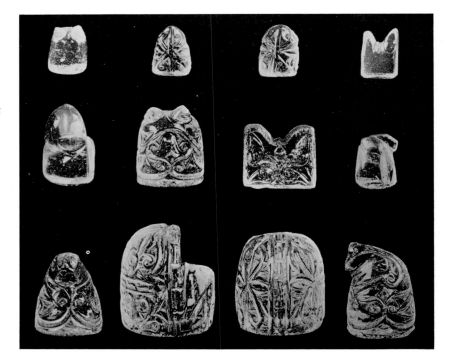

hard, however, to believe that the piece was made anywhere but in India. The great elaboration is not surprising, for many of the European ivory pieces made in the thirteenth century in Germany and elsewhere are very elaborate, too, perhaps in imitation of Indian pieces.

The general shapes of Persian chessmen remained for several centuries very close to those of the pieces found at Nishapur. Those from Egypt made of glass and ascribed to the tenth century, and other early pieces from Islamic countries, do show some changes. The horse became a more or less conical piece with a projecting head. The elephant lost its silhouette but retained the two small projections, which, however, became more and more removed from reality. The thronelike pieces of the *shah* and *firzan* of the ninth century disappeared, developing into taller turned forms as early as the eleventh century, as is evident in some Islamic pieces excavated at Mansura, near Hyderabad, India. Islamic pieces from other areas also became completely nonrepresentational, and the suggestion of a horse head or of an elephant died out, although the hornlike projections survive in some instances until the twelfth century. As for the rooks with their deep notch, this form continued for some time, as is proved by a fine glazed ceramic piece from Persia, of the thirteenth century, with painted and fretted patterns, that was in the collection of André Godard. The last of the resemblances died out, and the pieces, to Western eyes, are most confusing. It is interesting to note, however, that in a wooden set from Nigeria—a place visited by the traveler Ibn Batuta, who was born in Tangiers in the fourteenth century—the rook preserves the two pointed horns of the early *rukh*, though in an exaggerated form. The set (No. 39), made at the beginning of the twentieth century, came with a soft leather "board." An innovation, which may not be of Muslim origin, is that the king is distinguished from his counselor by having a piece of cloth wrapped around him.

The tendency toward stylization continued in Europe, with the elephant becoming unrecognizable for what it was, even sometimes having two small horse heads instead of tusks, as in an early piece from Dorset, now in the British Museum. An extraordinary development in the late twelfth century is to be seen in a bishop in the State Gallery, Frankfurt am Main, which, while decorated with figural scenes, is furnished with two projecting human heads, one of a man and the other of a woman, thereby preserving the old idea of projecting "horns." By the fifteenth century the European elephant had two hornlike projections and was called *cornutus* or *cornu.* In England there probably developed confusion between these projections and the miter, and we know that in Scandinavia and Scotland the bishop was in use from the twelfth century on. The projections of the rook were less pointed and sometimes drooped down and became leaflike, or, at times, not unlike butterfly wings. Very confusingly, these "wings" also developed into a pair of horse heads. In the sixteenth century the tower or castle was introduced. By the end of the fifteenth century, the knight with a true horse head appeared in these otherwise nonrepresentational sets, and by the early seventeenth century there were also double horse heads. The kings and queens developed in various ways, mostly as balusterlike forms, sometimes with surmounting crowns with crosses, which of course made them quite removed from their Islamic counterparts.

Pieces in human and animal form became fairly common in Europe in the twelfth and thirteenth centuries. A hoard of seventy-eight pieces in walrus ivory, discovered on the Island of Lewis in the western Hebrides off the west coast of Scotland, is now mostly in the British Museum, with some of the pieces in the Royal Scottish Museum in Edinburgh: seated kings, queens, and bishops, mounted knights, and armored men on foot—the rooks—bearing long shields pointed at the bottom. It is interesting that among these chessmen, which by their ornament can be dated to the twelfth century, the bishop already appears, although the word *auphin* was still current. It is clear that in Europe figural chessmen had at an early date certain iconographic differences from their Islamic predecessors. But there was a tendency in European figural kings and queens, no matter how elaborate, to keep the general outline of early Islamic chessmen.

Some impressive later pieces, including elaborately carved ivory ones of the thirteenth century, show that chess was played in the highest circles in Europe. That the original meaning of the pieces was not lost is also evident, for knights, chariots, and elephants appear carved in the round. It is interesting to see that certain large pieces representing kings, though seated on horses, are surrounded by subsidiary warriors, just as in the large "Charlemagne" piece made in the Orient. These chessmen of the medieval period vary considerably in quality, some being crude and provincial, and others, like a knight in the Metropolitan's collection (No. 7), showing very fine workmanship.

By the sixteenth century new subject matter was introduced, agreeing, as is natural, with the spirit of the time. By the end of the century themes such as Romans versus Barbarians came to the fore, and all connections with both the East and the medieval period were severed. For another thing, the geometrical base was introduced. Purposely exotic chessmen made an appearance, inaugurating a fashion that, as will be seen, was never to die.

During the eighteenth century, and on into the nineteenth, another spirit is to be seen in European representational chessmen. This was probably an echo of the romantic period, with a touch of classicism clinging to it. Many of the sets remind one that curio cabinets had become the rage in the eighteenth century. The impression given by such pieces is one of artificiality, a quality unknown in chessmen of the medieval period. The medieval pieces reflect a true romantic spirit proper to its time, whereas the later ones, no matter how precious and elegant, convey only a backward-looking glance at romanticism. The early sets, when of fine quality, indicate in a natural way the rank and importance of their owners; the later ones show a striving to produce something out of the ordinary. One sometimes has the feeling that those who made or commissioned them were looking for suitable subject matter in the same way that subjects for theses are now diligently sought for in universities. Whether the chessmen be old or late, however, they reflect the spirit of their times.

Roman history provided many subjects, which were sometimes realized in a masterly but nonetheless amusing way, giving the suggestion that the figures on the chessboard, as in No. 56, are playing parts in a royal masque. That they should appear in this fashion is not demeaning, for, from the Renaissance through the eighteenth century, some of the best artists and writers were engaged in such activities. Some of the battle sets of chessmen illustrate clearly the love of classicism that swept the arts in the eighteenth century and lasted into the nineteenth. Others portray well-known opponents, such as Henry VIII of England and Francis I of France. This set (No. 42) purports to represent the Field of the Cloth of Gold but is actually an excellent example of nineteenth-century presentation of old costume seen through German eyes. In others we find opponents who never met on the field of battle, such as Frederick the Great and Napoleon (No. 46). Some sets, however, even of the eighteenth century, illustrate contemporary wars, a custom that has lasted to the present day. Some of these sets were made almost as soon as the battle had been fought, such as No. 50, representing the Crimean War, while others appeared somewhat later, as those recalling the Napoleonic Wars (Nos. 40, 47, 48). The step from the production of such sets to those that were meant to influence public opinion was an easy one, and so we have Communists and Capitalists (No. 67) or a Hungarian set made to protest the yielding of Hungary's erstwhile territory at the treaty table of the

Trianon (No. 54). Somewhat earlier, this sort of thing seems to have been done more gracefully, if we may judge by No. 41, which has the men of Andreas Hofer on one side of the board and the troops of Napoleon on the other. Some sets of the present century are almost history lessons, that showing the Battle of Saratoga (No. 81), for instance. Even more so is this true of an enormous board for a set that was never finished, designed by Max Esser of Germany, which was commissioned by Mr. Pfeiffer to illustrate the American War of Independence; it is filled with all kinds of relevant material, including the names and dates of all the battles and the names of all the generals (Figure 9).

9. Chessboard designed by Max Esser, 1931–1939. Gift of Gustavus A. Pfeiffer, 48. 150

In the early centuries chess offered convenient metaphors for literary and even moral purposes, with the pieces closely allied to social rank, but the situation has changed greatly when the chessmen merely embody the characters of a play or book, with no metaphorical connection. We thus have from the eighteenth century Flaxman's magnificently modeled characters from Shakespeare's plays (No. 78), and from our own time the characters of *Alice in Wonderland* recreated by Sorcha Boru from Tenniel's illustrations (No. 79). In such sets the emphasis has become less on the playing of the game and more on the pieces themselves. Though in the process all remembrance of the original piece has vanished, those that have taken their place have other interesting meanings—some of which continue to be military.

A remarkable feature of the eighteenth, and even more of the nineteenth, century was the enormous production of chessmen in Asia for Europe and America. The skill of the Indian, Chinese, and other Oriental craftsmen seems to have stimulated them into producing more and more fanciful pieces. The Chinese, who themselves play, as we have seen, with the simplest of pieces, probably made the most elaborate ones, but the Indians were not far behind. Needless to say, a great many of them could not be used for play and were doomed from birth to grace the corner cabinet or to live under a glass cover. Many of them have a certain fascination, as sea captains and other travelers to the Orient have found out. The ivory carvers were adept at introducing a touch of the West into their productions. Portraits of the rulers of visiting foreigners would be carved on the kings so that we can see the later Georges, Edward VII, and, for French customers, Napoleon. The queens are not always given such careful attention, and can rarely be recognized as actual persons. They are usually dressed in Oriental fashion. In India, the Englishman showed he was not averse to being portrayed as a rather corpulent John Bull on the back of a horse or camel, and he delighted in buying elaborate pieces in the form of elephants with maharajahs riding in howdahs on their backs. Other pieces were based on English models of a conventional type and then elaborately carved in a graceful fashion, often with little touches that betray their Oriental origin.

India, having given the fundamentals of chess to the world so many centuries ago, has thus not been able to keep its own chess immune from the influence of others, Muslims or Europeans, but India must receive its due as the originator of the game. The game has changed, the shapes of the pieces have changed, and the names of the pieces are now legion. Many of the threads of these developments can be unraveled and followed, and though East may be East and West be West, chess is but one example of how inextricably intertwined they can be.

This catalogue, besides giving some historical aspects of chess and chessmen, provides information on the sets exhibited at The Brooklyn Museum in 1968. In addition to their origins and historical background, it gives material details, including particulars of manufacture, a matter usually ignored but one that may help to distinguish different sources for pieces that at first glance seem similar. The work of this nature has been done by Jessie McNab Dennis. She has corrected and added much to the information that accompanied the pieces to the Museum, which often included fanciful assertions about the sets' original owners and the date of their manufacture. There were, however, few facts to support this information, and several of the statements were demonstrably false.

The sets have been arranged in groups, of which the first includes early pieces—individual chessmen and the group discovered by the Metropolitan's Iranian Expedition. They are followed by all the Oriental sets, arranged for the most part by country of origin. Next come sets that illustrate actual battles and wars; then oppositions that often resulted in battle, such as that between Christians and Muslims. Oppositions of a more abstract nature follow, such as Good against Evil, and then those of a fanciful nature. Sets depicting episodes in American history have a section by themselves, and the catalogue closes with sets that are almost or completely nonfigural. Apart from its catalogue number, each set is given the accession number by which it is identified in the Metropolitan Museum. The donors of a few of the pieces are mentioned; all the other pieces are the direct or indirect gift of Gustavus A. Pfeiffer.

Several books are mentioned so often that they are referred to in abbreviated form. In full dress, they are: H. J. R. Murray, *The History of Chess* (Oxford, 1913); Donald M. Liddell with the collaboration of Gustavus A. Pfeiffer and J. Maunoury, *Chessmen* (New York, 1937); Alex Hammond, *The Book of Chessmen* (London, 1950); and Hans and Siegfried Wichmann, *Chess* (New York, 1964).

The idea of presenting a chess-set exhibition at this time (the third in which a large number of sets of the Pfeiffer Collection have been publicly displayed, and the first to have a catalogue) was that of Thomas P. F. Hoving, Director of The Metropolitan Museum of Art. The first such exhibition to have been held in The Brooklyn Museum, it was made possible through the close cooperation of the two museums and their directors, Mr. Hoving and Thomas S. Buechner.

Thanks for their help in solving particular problems in the preparation of the book are due to: Helmut Nickel, Curator of Arms and Armor; Stella Blum, Assistant Curator, The Costume Institute; Nora Scott, Associate Curator of Egyptian Art; and John Canonico, Senior Restorer, all of the Metropolitan Museum; Charles Froom of The Brooklyn Museum; Siegfried Wichmann of the Bavarian State Museum, Munich; Margaret Webster Plass, O.B.E., of the Department of Ethnography, British Museum; Shirley Bury of the Victoria and Albert Museum, London; the Reverend F. W. Peacock, of the Moravian Mission, Labrador; Marion Deane; Margaret Eppstein; and Jeffrey Blyth of the *London Daily Mail*; help in the identification of ivory and woods was given by Donald J. Dodelson, D.D.S., and B. F. Kukachka, in charge of the Wood Identification Research of the Forest Products Laboratory of the United States Department of Agriculture.

1 Elephant

Persian, VI–VII century. Black stone, carved in one piece with its oval base. H: 2⁷/₈ inches. Gift of Alastair Bradley Martin, 48.154.8

This piece is probably a chessman, but there is no proof for the supposition. If it truly is one, it is the earliest in existence.

Ex. coll. Ernst Herzfeld.

REFERENCES: E. Herzfeld, "Ein sasanidischer Elefant," *Archaeologische Mitteilungen aus Iran*, III (1931), 27; F. Sarre, "Sasanian Stone Sculpture," in *Survey of Persian Art*, Oxford, 1939, vol. I, pp. 593–600, vol. IV, pl. 169b.

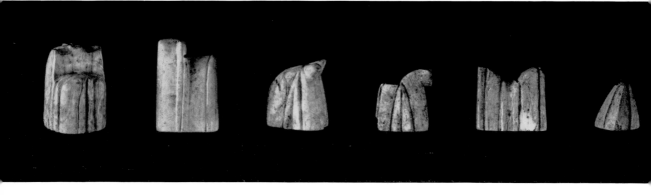

2   6 chessmen, green v. white

Persian (Nishapur), early IX century. Ivory, some stained green. H: tallest piece 1³/₈ inches, pawn ³/₄ inch.   40.170.148–151

The kings and queens are so formed that the rear part is higher than the front. It has been suggested that these are thrones, but the suggestion is not entirely satisfactory. It is perhaps possible that they represent seated figures. The king is more circular in section than the queen and may be from a different set. The bishops, elephants, have two projections that look more like horns than tusks, but the general silhouette is not unlike that of an elephant. The section is almost circular. The knights are roughly in the form of horses, much stylized but nonetheless recognizable. The rooks are rectangular and notched at the top, a form that is well known from the crystal pieces in the so-called "Charlemagne" set in Osnabrück (Murray, *History of Chess*, opp. p. 766). This shape lasted until at least the thirteenth century in Iran. The pawns are small pyramids with a vertical line on each face.

These chessmen, the earliest that can be positively dated, are very heavily stylized, though, as noted above, two of the pieces suggest the animals they were supposed to represent. There were undoubtedly figural pieces also, but none has survived beyond one of the Sasanian period (No. 1), which is earlier, and one of a later date (No. 3). There is plenty of evidence that the people of Nishapur were not averse to representing human and other living forms.

K, Q, B, KT, R, P

3 Chessman

Persian, XI century. Ivory, carved in one piece with its oval base. H: 4 inches.

65.53

The base is decorated with a pearled border. A man is mounted on a winged animal that has lost its head. The rider's head is also incomplete. He wears trousers with a crosshatched pattern, and his jacket has suggestions of folds. It is possible that this is not a knight but a *rukh*, a hero on a mythical animal. The piece was reputedly found in Saqqizabad.

4 Chessman

Probably Egyptian, xi–xii century. Ivory, with remains of green stain. H: 2¹/₄ inches.   47.68

Emerging from the center of the domed top is a squarish projection decorated on each face with a small circle and dot. The lower part of the piece has been cut away so that the words *al-Zahir* (the Victorious) show in relief. Above are simple patterns of dot and circle and a series of semicircles. This form of decoration also appears on a knight in the Cluny Museum, Paris, dated to the ninth or tenth century (Wichmann, *Chess*, pls. 10, 11). The date of this present piece must be later than that in view of the calligraphy. It is not certain what it represents, but it may be the shah (king). It is not a knight, bishop, or rook.

5   Elephant (bishop)

Spanish or Sicilian, XII century. Ivory, with incised decoration filled with black pigment. H: 3¹/₂ inches.   Gift of Alastair Bradley Martin, 49.36

Dots and circles are used to create decorative plantlike forms growing upward from an encircling band that contains an undulating stem with single leaves above and below it. The two projections near the rounded top show that the piece represents an elephant, the bishop in modern English parlance. The use of these projections to indicate the elephant goes back to the very beginning of the ninth century in Persia (see No. 2). This particular form was taken to Europe by the Arabs and persisted there through the twelfth century.

Ex coll.: Alphonse Kann, Paris; Jacob Goldschmidt, Berlin.

6   Bishop

English, XII century. Ivory, carved, with deep undercutting on the back. H: 3⁷/₈ inches.   Gift of J. Pierpont Morgan, 17.190.229

The enthroned bishop, vested in cope and miter, grasps a crozier in his left hand and gives benediction with his right. On either side, in a smaller scale, are attendants, one holding a book and the other what looks like a rod. The back of the throne, in two panels, is elaborately carved in a design of intertwining stems from which budlike foliations emerge.

The piece somewhat resembles some of the chessmen found on the Isle of Lewis, of which most are in the British Museum. It differs from them in that it is of true ivory whereas they are of walrus ivory and in that it has subsidiary figures while they do not. The awkwardness of the hand raised in benediction is, however, to be seen in a bishop of that group (Wichmann, *Chess*, pl. 43b), and the shape of the miter is identical. The carving is of finer quality in the present piece, and it may be a little later in date. The piece is very similar in style to a queen in the museum at Schwerin, Germany, illustrated in Goldschmidt, *Elfenbeinskulpturen* (1926), vol. IV, no. 244.

These early English and Scandinavian chessmen in the form of bishops show that although corruptions of the Arabic name of the piece, *al fil* (the elephant), persisted in literature as *alfin, aufin,* and so on, the character of the original piece, representing the elephant corps in an army, was lost.

REFERENCES: *The Metropolitan Museum of Art Bulletin*, XV (1920), 16, ill. p. 17; J. Breck, *The Pierpont Morgan Wing* (The Metropolitan Museum of Art, 1929), p. 50.

7 Knight

French, XIII century. Ivory, carved in one with its oval base, now without color.
H: 3¹/₈ inches.   Gift of J. Pierpont Morgan, 17.190.231

The figure is St. George killing the dragon, whose tail ends in foliate forms. St. George is clad in a cuirass over a tunic, and a closed helmet; he has a shield, pointed at the lower end. He once brandished a sword in his right hand, but the arm has been broken off at the shoulder. The sheath hangs down his left side.

This deeply undercut chessman is far more elegant than many of this date, in great contrast to German pieces and to a lesser degree to those of England and even to another French knight (see Wichmann, *Chess*, pls. 52, 54, 55). Pieces such as this would be used only in aristocratic circles. Contemporary with them were conventional nonfigural sets used by all social degrees.

Ex coll. Georges Hoentschel.

REFERENCE: André Pératé, *Catalogue of the Hoentschel Collection: Ivories* (Paris, 1911), no. 18, pl. xv, and note.

8 Elephant

Indian, XVIII century. Ivory, carved in one with its oval base. H: 2 inches.

Gift of J. Pierpont Morgan, 17.190.228

The upper part of the rider of the elephant is missing. The piece is probably from a playing set and not from one of those, such as Nos. 11 and 27, for sale to the Anglo-Indians. It could be earlier than the suggested date, but there is little evidence on which to base a surmise. Unlike most of the later sets, the top of the base curves down at the edges; later sets usually have flat bases and two riders on the elephants. The edge is very similar to that of the early nineteenth-century set from Rajasthan (No. 17). If the piece is late in date it may have functioned as a rook, if early, in its proper and original place—that now occupied by a bishop in English and American sets.

9 32 chessmen, red v. green

Indian, XVIII century. Ivory, turned and resist-dyed red and green with a diaper of trilobed leaf patterns in reserve. The bishops, made in three pieces joined by metal screws, appear to be replacements. One green knight was broken and repaired; its color is faded. H: king 2 inches, pawn 1¹/₈ inches.   48.174.106a–p, aa–pp

The spool-like shapes of the king, queen, and pawns are typical of Indian chessmen, and somewhat similar ones are illustrated by Thomas Hyde and shown again in Murray, *History of Chess*, p. 89, as coming from Surat on the coast north of Bombay, where the first British trading station was opened in 1612. The pieces representing elephants (bishops) in the late eighteenth century seem to have been bigger and more substantial than those of this set. Here they have the spindle-like shapes common in the nineteenth century. The set may be ascribed to the eighteenth century, with the bishops probably being later additions.

P, R, KT, B, Q, K

10 32 chessmen, red v. green

Indian, XVIII century. Turned ivory, stained red or green, with a geometrical floral pattern in silvering on the red pieces and in gilding on the green pieces. The pattern is now much worn. H: king 1³/₄ inches, pawn 1 inch.   48.174.7a–p, aa–pp

The set was made for use by Muslims, and there is no suggestion of what the pieces originally represented. The capital pieces are somewhat massive and, in decreasing measure, are king, queen, and rook (using Western nomenclature). The bishop and knight are more spindly, the bishop being the taller, and both exceeding the king in height, a peculiarity also to be seen in Kurdish sets (see Murray, *History of Chess*, p. 361, reproduced from S. Culin, *Chess and Playing Cards,* Washington, 1898).

The set was acquired by Mr. Pfeiffer in 1931 from Ganeshi Lall of Agra together with No. 12.

K, Q, B, KT, R, P

11 British and Hindus 32 chessmen, white v. black

Indian (Bengal), late XVIII century. Ivory, carved in one with their oval bases. The bases of the Hindu side are painted black. H: king 5 inches, pawn 3¼ inches.

48.174.116a–p, aa–pp

The kings, rajahs, are in elaborate howdahs with double domes and projecting awnings held by two inclined poles, a form of howdah that was still used in the early nineteenth century. The minister (queen) is in an open howdah but shaded by an umbrella. The original symbolism has been lost in this set, as is evident by the introduction of a lion on the British side in lieu of the elephant (bishop) and a rhinoceros on the Indian side—a peculiar innovation though the animal does exist in India. A cavalryman correctly acts as knight on the British side, and a cameleer with drawn sword, incorrectly, on the Indian side. The camel often appears in Indian chess sets in the position of the bishop, but not as the knight. The rooks are crenelated towers, with a soldier holding a flag on top. The pawns are standing soldiers, the British with muskets, the Hindus with long spears and round shields. The set, obviously, was not made for playing purposes.

A very similar set of the eighteenth century is illustrated in Murray, *History of Chess*, opp. p. 88. Another version is in Liddell, *Chessmen*, 4th ill. after p. 82. Yet another set with similar pieces is in the Victoria and Albert Museum, London (IM 42–1910), dated about 1790. It came from Berhampore, Bengal.

Hindu P, R, KT, B, K, Q

12   32 chessmen

Indian, XVIII–XIX century. Sheet silver, shaped and soldered into closed hollow forms, with repoussé patterns. H: king 2 inches, pawn 1 inch.

48.174.11a–p, aa–pp

The sides are distinguished by their different repoussé patterns. One has a four-petaled flower design on the tops of the major pieces, except the king and queen; on the tops and sides of these is an allover diaper of an almond-shaped motif, which is also on the tops of the pawns. The sides of the pawns are decorated with vertical lines. The other side has a petal design on the tops of all the pieces, pawns included; the sides of the king and queen have a diaper leaf motif. The sides of the pawns are decorated with a herringbone pattern.

This set is for Muslim use. According to Ganeshi Lall of Agra, from whom it was acquired by Mr. Pfeiffer in 1931, it was made for Diwan Todar May, in the period of Akbar (the Timurid ruler of Hindustan from 1556 to 1605). There is no proof of such an early date, but these shapes were in existence in the eighteenth century, as we know from Thomas Hyde's *Syntagma Dissertationem* (Oxford, 1767; see Murray, *History of Chess*, p. 89). The set should probably be ascribed to the reign of Akbar II (1806–1837).

P, R, KT, B, Q, K

13   32 chessmen, red v. green

Indian, XVIII–XIX century. Ivory, carved in one piece with their square bases, painted cream color (now much worn), with red or green details. H: king 3¼ inches, pawn 2 inches.

48.174.145a–p, aa–pp

Although it is figural, this set was made for playing. The kings kneel and hold scepters; the queens are represented by generals although they are called viziers or counselors, and they bear swords. The elephant, instead of being in his original position (next to the king), has, as is common in Indian chess, displaced the rook at the corner of the board. In his own place is a camel. The knight is represented by a horse head. The pawns are small standing men, unarmed, wearing kiltlike skirts.

R, KT, B, K, Q, P

14   32 chessmen, white v. green

Indian, XVIII–XIX century. Ivory, turned, drilled, and carved, made in several sections and assembled by threading. The green pieces were dyed after assembly. H: king 6³/₄ inches, pawn 3 inches.   48.174.37a–p, aa–pp

This set was modeled after eighteenth-century European chessmen and is remarkable in the height of the pieces, which renders the set impractical for play. The extreme height is shared by a set that this one closely resembles, in the London Museum, reputedly presented by James II to Samuel Pepys, which would also seem to be of Indian manufacture (Liddell, *Chessmen*, 7th ill. after p. 42). The Indian origin is betrayed here in the forms of the kings and of the kiosks that serve as rooks.

A nineteenth-century version of this type, of less elegance, is in Hammond, *The Book of Chessmen*, pl. XXIX. In discussing sets of this type, the author also says he believes that the set in the London Museum is of later date than James II, and of Indian manufacture.

P, K, B, KT, R

15 32 chessmen, green v. brown

Indian, XVIII–XIX century. Jade and brown striated onyx marble. H: king 2¹/₄ inches, pawn ⁷/₈ inch.   48.174.43a–p, aa–pp

The chessmen, which were cut on the lapidary's wheel from cylindrical shapes, are nonfigural except for the knight, which terminates in a horse's head, and the rook, which terminates in an elephant's head. The other pieces are balusterlike, the king, queen, and pawns being very similar in shape, diminishing in size. The bishops are spindle-like. The set shows a fusion of Hindu and European influences in a basic nonfigural set; the former in the displacement of the elephant as bishop and its identification with the rook. The horse head suggests English influence. The set was acquired in Bombay. A board that came with it has a molding and ball feet of gilt-bronze, and squares of jade and striated onyx marble, each inlaid in the center with mother-of-pearl stars.

B, KT, R, K, Q, P

16   Indians and Europeans   32 chessmen, red v. green

Indian (perhaps Pondicherry), second half of the XIX century. Ivory, carved figures, with details in polychrome lacquer and gilding, cemented to flat oval bases, dyed red or green. H: king 5 inches, pawn 3³/₈ inches.   48.174.113a–p, aa–pp

As often occurs in sets of this elaborate type, which were never made for play, there is no difference between the kings and the generals of the two sides. Only the pawns are clearly differentiated, the Indians holding long spears and girt with swords, the Europeans with muskets with fixed bayonets. Unlike Bengali sets of this period (see No. 27), the rooks are not boats but are castles with a flag-carrying infantryman on the top. The elephant's (bishop's) place is filled by a camel—a common feature in late Indian chess sets. The facial types suggest French soldiers.

Indian R, KT, B, K, Q, P

17   32 chessmen, red v. green

Indian (Rajasthan), early XIX century. Carved ivory, figures cemented to low flat bases with dentate edges, lacquered red and green, and gilt. H: king 7¹/₂ inches, pawn 2 inches.   48.174.94a–p, aa–pp

As is often the case with Indian sets made for foreigners, the principal pieces are in the same style on each side, but the pawns are differentiated. The kings, the ministers, and three of the camel-riders (bishops) have an attendant by the left foreleg of the elephant or camel on which they ride. The ministers' elephants hold lions in their trunks. On either side of their tall howdahs, the kings' and the ministers' elephants carry cannon. The rooks are elephants, as they often are in Hindu sets, and these hold an oversize horseshoe. For a European example of this differentiation of pawns, see No. 73.

A similar set in the Victoria and Albert Museum, London, is ascribed to Rajasthan, about 1800 (IM241–241EE–1922). As here, the men have heavily painted eyes. Another similar set, erroneously called Siamese, is in Liddell, *Chessmen*, 3rd ill. after p. 82. Some other similar sets have been attributed to Madras (Hammond, *The Book of Chessmen*, pl. XXIII).

Q, K

18   32 chessmen, red v. green

Indian (Jaipur), XIX century. Carved ivory, figures cemented to turned bases, which are stained red or green; details of the pieces in gilding and black and red paint. H: king 1³/₄ inches, pawn 1¹/₂ inches.   48.174.150a–p, aa–pp

The pawns, human male heads wearing turbans, have red or green forehead marks to match their bases. All the pieces are figural, and the arrangement—the king and minister being male half-figures, the bishop a camel, the knight a horse, and the rook an elephant—is exceedingly common in Indian chess.

P, R, KT, B, Q, K

19 32 chessmen, red v. black

Indian (Baroda), late XIX century. Ivory, carved in one piece with lobed oval bases. The bases are drilled with dot-and-circle motifs, filled with red or black paint. H: king 2½ inches, pawn 1½ inches. 48.174.18a–p, aa–pp

The principal pieces of the two sides are similar, but the pawns are distinguished by their headgear, being conical on one side and on the other having the tip hang down slightly. Otherwise the pawns are identical, all carrying round shields and drawn swords. The pieces are elaborate but nonetheless practical, unlike many Indian chessmen of the figural type. In accordance with the Indian custom in modern times, camels have taken the place of elephants (bishops). The camels carry two riders. As is common when camels are bishops, elephants are rooks, although in some Indian sets (like No. 11) castles are used, a result of British influence. The set shows two opposed factions and represents no particular military struggle.

P, R, KT, B, Q, K

20   32 chessmen, red v. black

Indian, XIX–XX century. Ivory, turned and polished, in two or more sections assembled by threading. Bands and dot-and-circle designs are made in red or black lacquer. H: king 2¹/₄ inches, pawn ³/₄ inch.   53.71.107a–p, aa–pp

The set is for Muslim players. As will be seen by comparison with other Indian Muslim sets, there are considerable variations in the shapes of these nonfigural pieces. None gives any indication of what it originally represented. By their size the king and queen gain a more important appearance; the rook is a diminutive edition of the same form.

R, KT, B, K, Q, P

21   32 chessmen, red v. green

Burmese, XVIII century. Carved ivory, painted red or green (now much worn). H:
king 2³/₄ inches, pawn 1³/₄ inches.   48.174.107a–p, aa–pp

The set, which was made for playing, is representational. The king is a
"Great King," here a seated figure. He has not a queen but a lieutenant general, also seated, with a small round shield in one hand. The elephant with
rider (bishop) represents, as it did in the original Indian game, the elephant
corps, and a horse and rider (knight) represents the cavalry. The pagoda-
like structure is the chariot, or rook. The pawns are foot soldiers. Burmese
sets are sometimes white and red, as well as green and red like this one.

   There are somewhat similar sets in the Victoria and Albert Museum, London, and the Pitt-Rivers Collection, Oxford (Murray, *History of Chess*, opp.
p. 111). A wooden set of similar type, with wheels on the chariots, is to be
seen in Hammond, *The Book of Chessmen*, pl. IX, where the elephants and
the chariots have been transposed.

P, R, KT, B, Q, K

22 Good and Evil   31 chessmen

Burmese, VXIII–XIX century. Ivory, carved and undercut. H: rook 2⁵/₈ inches, pawn
1³/₄ inches.   48.174.109a–d, f–p, aa–pp

Although both sides were left the natural color, they are distinguishable by
the form of the pieces. On the "good" side, the elephant (bishop) and horse
(knight) have monkey riders, whereas on the "evil" side they are without.
The "good" king is a protective spirit, and the "evil" one a demon. The
black pawns are also demons, and the white pawns are monkeys. The rooks
are chariots. Monkeys are used on the "good" side because in the Far East
they were thought to have the power to drive away or prevent the evil influences of wicked spirits. The "good" queen is missing.

TOP: "Good" R, KT, B, K, P, P.   BOTTOM: "Evil" R, KT, B, K, Q, P

23 32 chessmen, red v. white

Malayan, XIX century. Ivory, turned. The red pieces are dyed. H: bishop 1³/₄ inches, pawn ⁷/₈ inch. 48.174.103a–p, aa–pp

Following a common practice in sets made for Muslim players, the king, queen, and rook are the most massive pieces, diminishing in size. The bishops and knights have the lower part of the same height as the rooks but are the tallest of the pieces. The pawns are half the height of the bishops. The shape of these pieces is very similar to those of a set illustrated in Murray's *History of Chess*, p. 106, fig. 1. It is by no means the only form used in Malaya (see *ibid.* opp. p. 105). The translations of the names of the pieces are king, counselor, elephant, horse, chariot, and foot soldier (*budaq*, taken from the Arabic *bidaq*). The game thus retains its original meaning.

K, Q, B, KT, R, P

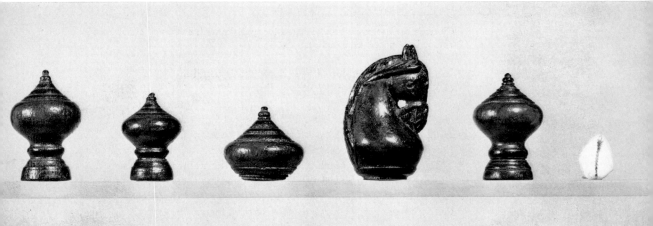

24 32 chessmen, red v. black

Cambodian, xx century. Teak, turned; the knight is carved and has a turned base. One side is varnished, the other painted black. The pawns are cowrie shells. H: knight 2 inches, pawn ½ inch.   53.71.203a–p, aa–pp

One player would have the shells for pawns with the aperture up, the other with it down. The knights alone give an indication of the original meaning of the game; they are the tallest pieces. Below the mane a classical leaf is set along the horse's back, probably an intrusion from Western art. The names of the pieces, translated, are lord, minister, nobleman, horse, and boat. In the last piece there is a correspondence with chess in Bengal, Java, and Annam, and also Russia, the sole country in Europe to substitute a boat for the rook. It has been pointed out that in Siam, Annam, and Russia, in the past, the principal means of transport was by water, and hence boats take the place of chariots or carts. When playing, the kings face the opponent's queen, and the pawns are placed two rows in front of the major pieces, leaving an empty row between them. Similar pieces are used in Siam.

For somewhat similar sets, see Liddell, *Chessmen*, 4th ill. after p. 90, and Wichmann, *Chess*, pl. 120.

K, Q, R, KT, B, P

25 32 chessmen, red v. blue

Chinese, XVIII–XIX century. Turned ivory disks with engraved characters filled with red or blue paste. D: 1 inch; H: 7/16 inch.   48.174.55a–p, aa–pp

The red and blue color of the characters is usual in Chinese ivory sets. In the cheaper wooden ones they are yellow and brownish black. The pieces represent: general, counselors, elephants, assistants, horses, chariots, cannons and catapults, and foot soldiers. They are placed on the intersections of the lines, and between the two sides of the board is a space called (Yellow) River. Thus there are ninety places, instead of sixty-four as in the Western game.

The substitution of simple disks with the names upon them can be considered the final change from figural chessmen, such as once were used in China, to conventional pieces. The Chinese figural pieces illustrated below were made to satisfy foreign, not Chinese, taste.

26 32 chessmen, white v. red

Chinese, late XIX century. Turned ivory disks with a carved emblem at the center, with background diapered in a pierced trellis design. One side is dyed red. D: 1³/₈ inches; H: 5/16 inch.   48.174.158a–p, aa–pp

The set was made for the English trade. It is interesting in that in embodying the conventional English symbols on disks, it is conforming with the Chinese custom of using ivory or wooden disks identified by ideograms.

K, Q, B, KT, R, P

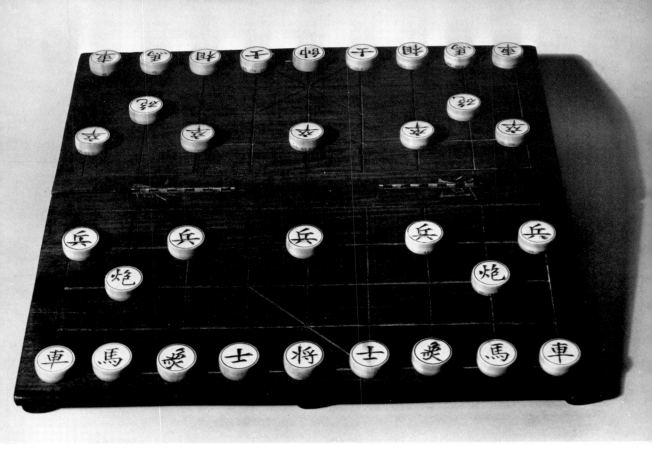

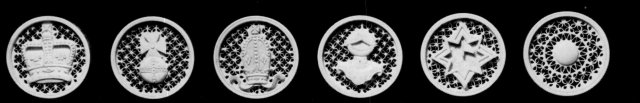

27   British and Hindus   32 chessmen, red v. green

Indian (Bengal), late XVIII–early XIX century. Ivory, carved in one with their oval, reel-shaped bases and painted in polychrome, mostly red and green. H: king 3 inches, pawn 1¹/₂ inches.   48.174.151a–p, aa–pp

The British have red jackets and green bases, the Indians green jackets and red bases. Both kings consist of an elephant with mahout, and a rajah with a second figure in an open howdah. The queens are similar, except that neither figure is a rajah. On the camels, as bishops, are a Hindu on the red side and a John Bull-like figure on the green. The knights are horses, and the rooks are boats, an Indian one with a pagoda-like awning and a British cutter with mast and rudder, both with small figures. The Hindu pawns hold swords and wear pleated skirts; the British pawns are infantrymen with muskets.

The use of boats instead of chariots is a somewhat late innovation in Indian chess, found in a few other Oriental countries, Siam and Annam, for example. The only European country in which it occurs is Russia, a phenomenon for which no very convincing explanation has yet been produced. Trade connections with India were, however, established in the reign of Ivan the Terrible (1544–1584) and continued later, although no territorial claims were established, and perhaps this has some bearing on the problem. The replacement of the original elephant (bishop) by a camel is common in Indian figural sets. It also appears in the nomenclature of the nonfigural pieces in the greater part of central Asia and the Deccan, and in Mongol chess. In Indian chess where the boat is not used as the rook, the elephant functions in its stead.

Sets such as this, representing an opposition of British and Indians, and elegantly carved, were probably made especially for British clients. The set is reputed to have belonged to the famous first governor of India, Warren Hastings (1732–1818), whose career was centered in Bengal, but no proof for this suggestion exists. The period, however, would seem correct.

For a somewhat similar set see Hammond, *The Book of Chessmen*, pl. XXIV.

Back: British B, R. Front: Hindu Q, P, R

28　Hindus and English　　32 chessmen, white v. black

Indian, late xix century. Ivory, turned, drilled, carved, and undercut, made in several sections and assembled by threading. The pieces on the dark side are ebonized.
H: king 5¹/₄ inches, pawn 3¹/₄ inches.　　　48.174.117a–p, aa–pp

The design of the set follows European models but has been elaborated in such a florid way that the chessmen could not be used for play. The pieces are easily recognizable despite the elaboration and the Oriental touches in the rooks, with their rosebud domes and Indian arcades. The major pieces are versions of the "crow's-nest" type common in Europe in the sixteenth century, but which began even earlier. Normally the points of the serrations project upward, but here they curl over and hang downward. The king's crown is a representation of an English one, two crossed straps with an orb at the point of juncture, rising from crosses patté with fleur-de-lis between. A French set of the late eighteenth century illustrated in Hammond, *The Book of Chessmen*, pl. xxx, shows the type of which this is an Indian elaboration, made for British purchasers. The British pawns are soldiers presenting arms; the Indians are spearmen with swords and shields.

KT, P, K, R

29   32 chessmen, white v. red

Chinese, XIX century. Ivory, carved in one piece with their high oval bases. H: king
4³/₄ inches, pawn 2³/₄ inches.   48.174.75a–p, aa–pp

The rooks are elephants with circular towers on their backs surmounted by
flags; a mahout sits on the elephant's head. The elephants are carved in a
curiously wooden manner, far less skillfully than the horses with which the
Chinese were familiar. The bases are deeply undercut to form an open design
of flowers and leaves. Chinese ivory sets are often carved with great skill and
furnished with ornamental bases, some, like these, being foliated. In others
carved balls are incorporated in the baluster support (see No. 30), or movable
concentric balls. These sets were made as gifts for foreigners, or for sale to
them, and well-known foreign personages were incorporated into many of
them. Others, such as this, consist entirely of Chinese figures, usually with
some of the characteristics of the Manchu dynasty, which reigned through-
out the nineteenth century and on to 1912. It has been suggested that some
of these sets represent Chinese versus Mongols, but the iconographical details here do not bear out the suggestion—it is a fanciful opposition.

R, KT, B, K, Q, P

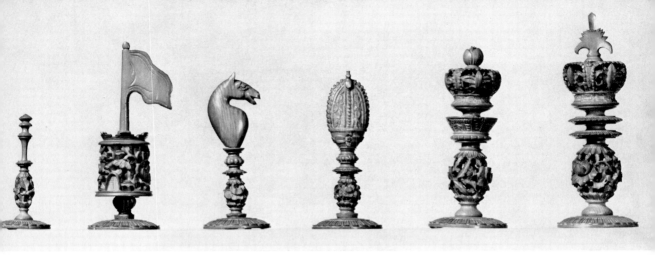

30   32 chessmen, white v. red

Chinese (Macao), XIX century. Ivory, turned, carved, and undercut, made in sections and assembled by threading. The red dye was applied after assembly. H: king 3³⁄₈ inches, pawn ⁷⁄₈ inch.   48.174.164a–p, aa–pp

These chessmen with baluster stems and finials denoting the rank of the piece are based on European models; the work, however, is unmistakably Oriental. The kings and queens are indicated by crowns, and the bishops by miters; the knights are horse heads, and the rooks have the form of crenelated towers with large flags at the top. The pawns are slim and elegant. The baluster stands all feature a carved, pierced, and undercut knop, which in the rook forms the mass of the tower. The bases are typical of many Chinese sets.

These chessmen are said to have once belonged to Eugène Sue (1804–1859), author of *The Mysteries of Paris* and *The Wandering Jew*. For similar sets see Hammond, *The Book of Chessmen*, pls. XXI, XXII.

REFERENCE: Liddell, *Chessmen*, 9th ill. after p. 42.

P, R, KT, B, Q, K

31 Europeans and Chinese   32 chessmen, white v. green

Chinese (Macao), XIX century. Ivory, carved heads threaded to turned and carved stands. The green pieces were dyed after assembly. H: king $4^{1}/_{8}$ inches, pawn $2^{5}/_{8}$ inches.   48.174.152a–p, aa–pp

The European king and queen, possibly Carlos I of Portugal and Queen Marie Amélie, are represented by crowned heads, the bishop by an episcopal head wearing an orientalized miter. Their opponents are Chinese, the king with an elegantly fretted headdress. Both knights are horse heads of a type common in European chess sets of the eighteenth and nineteenth centuries. An echo of Chinese chess, which has pieces named cannons, is in the mortars surmounted by flags for the rooks. The pawns are heads of Europeans or Chinese on baluster stands. The type of chessmen composed of balusters surmounted by human heads appears also in Bosnia-Herzegovina in the nineteenth century (Wichmann, *Chess*, pl. 156). Pieces of this type are practical for play. The theme is obviously Europeans and Chinese; the combination of Occidental and Oriental features has been satisfactorily accomplished.

Chinese R, KT, B, K, Q, P

32 32 chessmen, white v. red

Chinese, late XIX century. Ivory, carved figures on oval bases cemented to stands threaded to pulley-shaped bases. The red pieces were dyed after assembly. H: king 4¹⁄₈ inches, pawn 2¹⁄₈ inches.   48.174.165a–p, aa–pp

The white king portrays Napoleon, easily recognized by his posture and costume. His queen, however, cannot be identified as Josephine or Marie-Louise, and her dress is at least semi-Oriental. In many Chinese sets for export the likeness of the king is that of a well-known character, but the likeness does not extend to his consort (see No. 33). The opposing, Chinese, ruler is not recognizable, as is customary. The white bishop is evidently meant to be such; a Chinese sage is his opponent. Apart from these capital pieces there is considerable confusion. The four knights are the same shape, differentiated only by color; so are the rooks (elephants with castles). Somewhat archaistic in view of Napoleon's presence, the pawns are pikemen on the Chinese side, and their opponents carry swords and round shields, echoing some of the figures of Indian export sets. The set was undoubtedly made for French consumption, as the Chinese varied the nationality of the king to suit the allegiance of their visitors.

White R, KT, B, K, Q, P

33 30 chessmen, white v. red

Chinese (Canton?), early xx century. Ivory, carved in one with their octagonal bases. The red pieces are dyed. H: king 4½ inches, pawn 4⅛ inches.

48.174.122a, c–f, h–p, aa–pp

The meaning of this set is not clear. The red king, Edward VII, and a very Chinese-looking Queen Alexandra, who nevertheless wears European dress, are accompanied by an episcopal figure whose vestments have not been understood. The knights have very Chinese-looking horses with a hair tuft beneath the mouth (these pieces may be substitutions from another set). The men suggest English dragoons in the uniform of the period 1825 to 1860. The rooks are tall fenestrated edifices like lighthouses, surmounted by a flag. East and West are strangely combined in the pawns, which are distinctive of no particular country. The nature of the white side is equally hard to determine. No opponent of Edward VII would seem to be embodied in the king, though he carries a European scepter. The queen seems Oriental, and the bishop is of a different character from his opponent and might conceivably be meant to be a Russian or Greek bishop rather than a Roman one. The tower also incorporates Greek elements, Doric columns, for example, a reflection of European neoclassicism. Again the pawns are curious hybrids of Oriental and Occidental parentage. Both white knights are missing.

Red KT, K, white Q, K

34 41 chessmen

Japanese, xx century. Polished wood tablets with engraved characters filled with black lacquer. L: king 1 3/16 inches, pawn ⁷/₈ inch.   48.174.66a–t, aa–tt, aaa

This is the standard set for playing Japanese chess. The Japanese game bears some resemblance to Chinese chess in that it is played with inscribed pieces. It differs, however, in that there is no "river" between the two sides, and also in the moves. The board is rectangular, consisting of nine rows of nine rectangles, in which the pieces are set, rather than on the intersections of lines as in Chinese and Korean chess. The elaborate figural sets such as Nos. 35 and 36 were made only for foreign use.

There are twenty pieces on each side, arranged in three rows, as follows: back: fragrant wagon, honorable horse, silver, gold, king, gold, silver, honorable horse, fragrant wagon; middle: flying wagon, flying horse; front: foot soldiers. The pieces called "silver" and "gold" are generals. There is no difference in color between the sides; the direction in which the pieces are pointed—toward the opposing side—identifies the side to which they belong. The game is described in C. F. Wilkes, *Japanese Chess* (Memphis, Tenn., 1950).

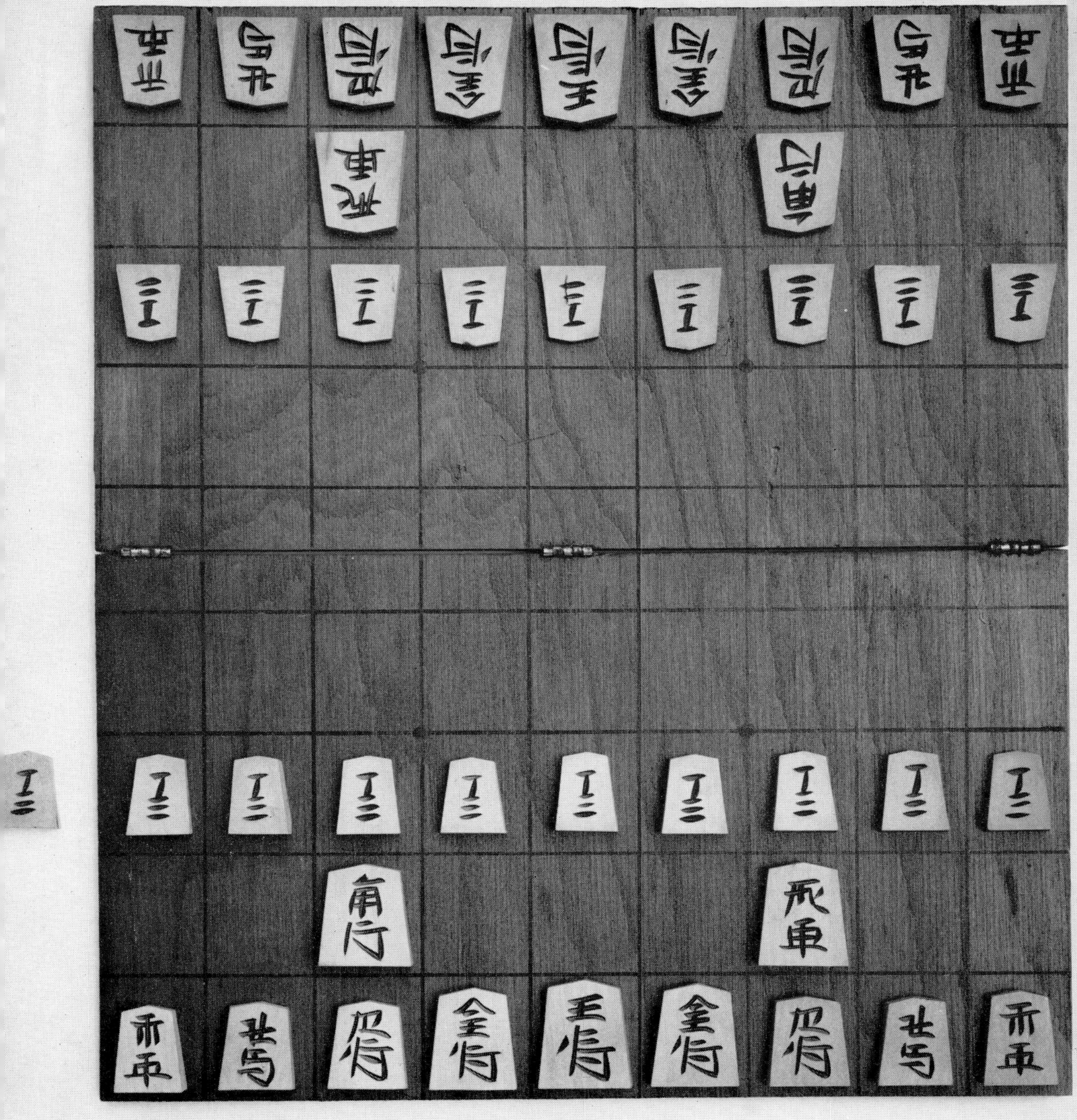

35 32 chessmen, white v. brown

Japanese, late XIX century. White and brown chalcedony; turned pedestals and bases plugged and cemented to half-figures cut and polished on the lapidary's wheel. H: king 3 inches, pawn 2¹/₈ inches. 48.174.8a–p, aa–pp

The king, knights, and pawns are all warriors, the queen a lady, and the bishops shaven priests. Exceptionally, there is no suggestion of a horse in the knights. The rooks consist of square towers surmounted by two incurving hornlike projections, which on Chinese and Japanese buildings are sometimes in the form of fish. In the following entry these same details appear on the top of one of the towers borne by the elephants. The cutting of the ball element of the pedestals suggests the cutting common in Chinese ivory sets. The set was acquired in Shanghai between 1920 and 1939 and probably was made in Japan for Chinese re-export.

R, KT, B, K, Q, P

36   32 chessmen, red v. white

Japanese, XIX–XX century. Red or white coral, carved in one piece with their high round bases, polished on the lapidary's wheel. H: king $3^5/8$ inches, pawn $1^7/8$ inches.
48.174.160a–p, aa–pp

The only differentiation between the sides is the color of the coral. The style of dress is archaistic, suggesting eighteenth-century Chinese costume. The rooks are elephants with small pagodas on their backs, with incurving projections at the top like those on the rooks in No. 35. The set was made for export and was acquired in Shanghai, whither it had initially been sent. For a true Japanese set see No. 34.

R, KT, B, K, Q, P

37 32 chessmen, white v. red

Persian, about 1930. Wood, turned and carved, painted in polychrome and black lacquer and gilded. H: king 2¹/₂ inches, pawn 1³/₄ inches.   48.174.104a–p, aa–pp

The set is nonfigural but for the horse-head knights. European influence is shown in the rooks in that they are towers with crenelations. The king, queen, and pawns are in the typical modern Muslim tradition, and the painted decoration is entirely Persian in style. There are lead weights in the bases to give the pieces greater stability.

P, R, KT, B, Q, K

38 32 chessmen, red v. gold

Algerian, XIX century. Sheet copper and brass, cut and soldered into open hollow forms with punched patterns. H: king 1 15/16 inches, pawn 1 1/8 inches.

53.71.8a–p, aa–pp

Rings and beads, size, and shape distinguish the different ranks of the pieces in this Algerian set. There appears some relationship to European chessmen, in the towerlike rooks, and especially in the knights with double horse heads such as appear in some German sets of the nineteenth century (see No. 95).

REFERENCE: Hammond, *The Book of Chessmen*, pl. XVIII.

R, KT, B, K, Q, P

39   32 chessmen, white v. brown

Nigerian (Bornu Province), xx century. Whittled limba wood, singed for the dark side. H: king 7 inches, pawn 1 inch.   48.174.102a–p, aa–pp

The kings and queens are similar, the kings being distinguished by a "robe" of blue striped cotton. The pieces show strong Islamic influence, which is to be expected as the people of Bornu Province are in the main Muslims. There had been contact between Islam and Nigeria for many centuries—Nigeria was visited by the famous traveler Ibn Batuta, who was born in Tangiers in the fourteenth century. The long ears of the rook are an exaggeration of the early form (see No. 2). Interestingly, these long ears also appear on conventional pieces from Scandinavia to which a fourteenth-century date has been assigned (J. F. Harbeson, *Nine Centuries of Chessmen*, Philadelphia, 1964, no. 12). The form of the pawns goes back to early Muslim times also. There is a goatskin board that came with the set, with squares demarcated by incised lines and dyed alternately cream and dark tan; it is slotted at the corners to allow it to be tied down.

White K, Q, P, brown P, KT, R, white B

40   The Battle of the Pyramids, 1803   32 chessmen

French, about 1870. Carved ivory, painted in polychrome gouache. H: king 4³/₄
inches, pawn 3¹/₈ inches.   48.174.84a–p, aa–pp

The kings represent Napoleon and the Mameluke ruler of Egypt, the queens
Josephine and the Egyptian queen. The bishops are humorous figures, play-
ing horn, cymbals, or tambourine; one holds a falcon, painted like a parrot.
The pawns of both sides are fighting men, each a different model.

Egyptian K, B, French K, Q

41   The Rebellion of Andreas Hofer   32 chessmen, blue v. pink

Austrian (Grödner Tal, Tyrol), early XIX century. Carved conifer wood figures cemented to slightly domed round bases, painted in gouache polychrome, blue and pink predominating. H: rook $3^1/_2$ inches, pawn $2^7/_8$ inches.   48.174.135a–p, aa–pp

The blue side represents Andreas Hofer and the Tyroleans, the pink side France. The rooks are camels for the blue side, elephants for the pink, with towers on their backs.

Andreas Hofer (1767–1810) was a Tyrolean patriot. He was fanatically devoted to Austria and resented the transfer of the Tyrol to Bavaria. He led a peasant revolt against the combined Bavarian and French armies, defeating them at Sterzing in 1809. Later, after Austrian reoccupation, the Tyrol was again threatened by France and Bavaria, but eventually Hofer entered Innsbruck in triumph. Nonetheless the Tyrol was ceded by Austria, and Hofer was captured by the Italian troops in the service of France and shot. The grimmer side of this story is not reflected in this set except by the military pieces. Austria later recovered the Tyrol, but parts of it were lost again after the first World War. The area in which the set was made is now incorporated into the north Italian province of Bolzano.

Back: French K, Tyrolean P, R; front: Tyrolean K, KT, B

42   The Field of the Cloth of Gold, 1520: Henry VIII and Francis I
32 chessmen, silver v. gold

German, second half of the XIX century. Cast silver, figures soldered to reel-shaped bases; the English side is gilded. The kings and queens are set with colored brilliants. H: king 3³/₄ inches, pawn 2¹/₄ inches.   53.71.83a–p, aa–pp

"Historical" sets of this type, fashionable in the nineteenth century, were not particularly suitable for playing but were excellent as subjects of conversation when put in the curio cabinet or otherwise exhibited.

REFERENCE: Liddell, *Chessmen*, p. 72 and 9th ill. after p. 74.

TOP: English R, KT, B, K, Q, P.   BOTTOM: French R, KT, B, K, Q, P

43   The Revolt of the Netherlands   32 chessmen, white v. brown

Dutch, about 1840–1850. Ivory, carved figures on irregular bases; the principal pieces are cemented to hand-carved faceted baluster stems, in turn cemented to slightly domed, faceted, octagonal bases; the pawns are cemented directly to flat octagonal bases. H: king 3 inches, pawn 1⁷/₈ inches.   53.71.104a–p, aa–pp

The kings probably represent Frederick Henry, prince of Orange (1584–1647), and Charles V of Spain (1500–1558). The queens' costumes are of an earlier style than the men's, and the queens are probably not intended to represent actual women. The period of Frederick Henry is considered the golden age of the Dutch republic. He continued the struggle for independence started by his father, William of Orange. Frederick died a few months before the completion of the treaty by which the United Provinces gained their independence from Spain in 1648. The earlier phase of the struggle is illustrated by the dark side, the king here wearing the crown of the Empire. There is thus an anachronism between the two sides, carried through in the sixteenth-century costume of the Spanish and seventeenth-century costume of the Dutch.

Spanish R, KT, B, K, Q, P

English, made by Phyllis and Delphis Gardner especially for Gustavus A. Pfeiffer, 1932. Carved yew wood painted in oil and varnished. H: king 3³/₄ inches, pawn 1¹/₂ inches.   48.174.143a–p, aa–pp

The pieces are very fully identified and their position in the side indicated by inscriptions cut on the underside of the bases. In addition, many pieces bear legends painted on streamers or pennants.

English king: Francis Drake Commander in Chief WK, (on pennants) *Circumnavigatio orbis* and *Time to finish our game of bowls and beat the Spanish too,* (on ship's flag) *Golden Hind*

queen: Queen Elizabeth WQ

bishops: Martin Frobisher WKB; and Lord Howard, Lord High Admiral WQB

knights: WKKT, (on pennants) *Sir John Hawkins* and *Victory;* and WQKT, (on pennants) *Vanguard* and *Sir Wm. Wynter*

rooks: Beachey Head WKR; and Skerry WQR

pawns (on flags or pennants): *Lord Thomas Howard, Golden Lyon; Nederland Hollandia; Thomas Drake; Seymour, Ark Royall; Revenge; Triumph; Palmer, Antelope; Chichester, James Fenner, Castle of Comfort*

Spanish king: King Philip II BK

queen: The Spanish Inquisition BQ

bishops: Perez Guzman Duque de Medina Sidania BKB; and Duque de Parma BQB

knights: Flagship of the Biscay Squadron BKKT, (on pennants) *San Juan Batista* and *Miguel de Recalde;* and Largest of the Great Galleons BQKT, (on pennant) *Reganzona*

rooks: Flagship of the Transports BQR, (on pennant) *Gran Grifon;* and The Great Galleons of Naples BKR, (on pennant) *La Galeaza Napolitana*

pawns (on pennants): *San Felipe; Nuestra Señora del Pilar; Duque de Florencia* (with BKBP underneath); *Nuestra Señora del Rosario, Pedro de Valdez; San Martin; San Luiz* (with BKKP underneath); *San Cristobal; Levanti, Alfonso de Leina, Varata Coronada*

In accordance with the McKinley Tariff Act of 1897, ruling that imported wares must be marked with their country of origin, each piece has "Made in England" handwritten in ink on the base. For another set by the Misses Gardner, see No. 49.

TOP: English R, KT, B, K, Q, P.   BOTTOM: Spanish R, KT, B, K, Q, P

45   Prussians and Hungarians   32 chessmen, silver v. gold

German, XIX century. Base metal, cast in one with their round bases, silvered or
silver-gilt. H: king 4³/₄ inches, pawn 2⁷/₈ inches.   53.71.43a–p, aa–pp

Although Pfeiffer published this set (Liddell, *Chessmen*, p. 71, ill. opp. p. 67)
as representing the intention of Frederick the Great to go to war against the
Turks, there is no evidence to support this statement. The uniforms on the
side he called Turkish are more characteristic of Hungary, and although the
uniforms on the Prussian side are correct, there is no detail on the figure of
the king to identify it with Frederick the Great. The pieces bear silver marks
on the bottoms of the bases, I G M (wrongly given as I C M by Pfeiffer), and
the assay mark of the city of Halberstadt. However, since these are cast
rather than punched, and the metal is not silver but base metal, the mid-
eighteenth-century date of the maker's mark need not be taken as the date
of manufacture of the pieces. For technical reasons, the pieces would seem to
date from the nineteenth century.

Hungarian R, KT, B, K, Q, P

46   Military Geniuses: Napoleon and Frederick the Great
32 chessmen, silver v. black

French, probably about 1840–1850. Iron, cast in one piece. The pieces for the "silver" side are pewtered (now much worn). H: king $2^5/8$ inches, pawn $1^1/2$ inches.

53.71.55a–p, aa–pp

The silver king is Napoleon (1769–1821), the silver bishop a French grenadier. The black king is Frederick the Great of Prussia (1712–1786) with his famous walking stick; the black bishop is a Prussian grenadier in a uniform combining eighteenth- and nineteenth-century features. The queens are crowned but not otherwise particularized. The pawns are in civilian, not military, dress. The theme of the opposing sides in this set is anachronistic, as Napoleon and Frederick were not contemporaries.

Black R, KT, B, K, Q, P

47   The Battle of Austerlitz, 1805   32 chessmen, red v. green

French (Dieppe?), early XIX century. Carved ivory figures cemented to small square
bases, which are dyed red or green. The figures retain a few traces of paint. H:
king 4³/₄ inches, pawn 2⁵/₈ inches.   48.174.131a–p, aa–pp

The red king is Napoleon, his queen Josephine. The red bishops are soldiers in tricornes. The red knights are French hussars, and the rooks are
figures personifying Victory, holding victor's wreaths, on high columns. The
pawns are French guardsmen. The green king is possibly Francis I of Austria,
and the queen may be his wife, but she resembles Catherine the Great of
Russia; her appearance here may be an anachronistic attempt to symbolize
the presence of Russia as an ally of Austria at the Battle of Austerlitz. The
knights are similar to Polish lancers; the rooks castles, the pawns Prussian
infantry. The figures are finely carved, and there is more animation and
sculptural quality in the queens and bishops than is customarily seen in chess
sculpture.

French R, KT, B, K, Q, P

48   The Battle of Waterloo   32 chessmen, white v. red

French (Dieppe), XIX century. Ivory, carved half-figures pinned and cemented to turned baluster stems, which are threaded to spreading circular bases. The red pieces are dyed. H: rook 3 inches, pawn 1³/₄ inches.   48.174.6a–p, aa–pp

Since this is a French set, the white figures, not surprisingly, represent Napoleon and the French, the red figures the British. The white king is Napoleon himself, and the queen is perhaps meant to be Marie-Louise. The bishops are *fous,* or jesters, as is usual in French sets, with standard lopsided faces. The soldiers for Napoleon's pawns are anachronistically shown in hats of the seventeenth century. The red king is Wellington; his pawns are grenadiers. Hammond, *The Book of Chessmen,* pl. XLVI, shows a similar set.

English R, KT, B, K, Q, P

49 The Greek War of Independence, 1821–1833   32 chessmen,
white v. green

English, made by Phyllis and Delphis Gardner, about 1929. Carved boxwood,
painted in polychrome oil paints. H: king 3⅝ inches, pawn 1⅞ inches.

53.71.11a–p, aa–pp

Some of the pieces are inscribed in letters cut on the underside in Greek:
Greek knight, Lord Byron holding a scroll marked *The Isles of Greece*:

O ΛOPΔOΣ BYPΩN (Lord Byron)

rooks: AΘHNAI (Athens) and METEΩPA (Meteora)

one pawn: O KΩΣTAΣ (Latin "custos," shepherd)

Turkish king: O ΣOYΛTANOΣ TΩN TOYPKΩN (the Turkish Sultan)

queen: H ΣOYΛTANA TΩN TOYPKΩN (the Turkish Sultana)

one bishop: O MOYΦTEΣ (the mufti)

knights: O ΣΠAHΣ (Turkish "spahi," horseman) [the inscription on the
other knight is indecipherable]

rooks: H ΠOΛIΣ (the city) and POYMHΛI XIΣΣAP (Rumeli Hissar)

Byron died at Missolonghi in 1824. Meteora in Thrace is famous for its
monasteries on top of lofty rocks, probably used for purposes of war. The
Rumeli Hissar is a fortress built by Sultan Muhammad II in 1452. It still
stands on the Asian side of the Bosporus.

Phyllis (born 1890) and Delphis (born 1900) Gardner were both sculptors,
daughters of Professor E. A. Gardner, the Greek archaeologist. They studied
at the Slade School of Art in London and were both active in the Arts and
Crafts movement. One of their specialties was chess sets illustrating famous
battles in history; many of these were exported to the United States. They
were co-owners of the Asphodel Press. For another of their sets see No. 44.

TOP: Greek K, Q, B, KT, R, P.   BOTTOM: Turkish K, Q, B, KT, R, P

French, about 1855. Turned and carved ivory, made in several sections and assembled by threading. The red pieces are dyed. H: tallest king 4 inches, pawn 2 inches.
47.174.65a1–a18, b1–b9, c1–c18, d1–d18

This set, which, according to the card acquired with it, was made for Napoleon III, is for the game of Oriental War. Played on a board of 117 squares (nine by thirteen), it has twenty-seven white pieces and thirty-six red pieces. Each side has nine principal figures and nine knights, and there are nine white pawns and eighteen red pawns. The nine principal pieces of each side include five historical figures. The white side, the coalition against Russia, has Napoleon III, the Sultan Abdul Mejid of Turkey, Queen Victoria, Marshal Pelissier of France, and General Alfonso La Marmora of Sardinia; the other principal pieces are the standards of France, Turkey, and Great Britain, and a tower representing Paris. On the Russian side are the Emperor Alexander II, the Empress Alexandra Feodorovna, Prince Michael Gorchakov, Grand Duke Constantine, and Prince Paskievitch (Russian commanders); also, three Russian standards and a tower representing St. Petersburg.

The game of Oriental War is said to have been invented in 1855 by François Gilot, a French watchmaker at Civray near Vienne. The object of the game was to capture the tower representing Paris or St. Petersburg; the towers were nonmoving pieces.

There is a box board *en suite,* inlaid in silver with the French Napoleonic eagle and the legend *Jeu de la Guerre d'Orient au double échec.*

REFERENCE: Liddell, *Chessmen,* pp. 98, ill. opp. p. 111.

Sultan Abdul Mejid of Turkey, Queen Victoria, Napoleon III, Alexander II

51 The Franco-Prussian War, 1870   32 chessmen, silver v. black

German, late XIX century. Bronze, cast in one piece with their stands. The "silver" side is pewtered. H: king 3¹/₈ inches, pawn 1⁵/₈ inches.   53.71.61a–p, aa–pp

The silver king represents Wilhelm I (King of Prussia in 1870, and in 1871 Emperor of Germany), and the queen, Queen Augusta. The black king is Emperor Napoleon III and his queen the Empress Eugénie. The two kings and queens are very creditable portraits, considering the scale and technique in which they are rendered. In particular, the Empress Eugénie is successful in suggesting the elegance of dress and bearing for which she was famous.

German R, KT, B, K, French Q, German P

52 Germany and Russia   32 chessmen, white v. red

German, late XIX century. Carved ivory figures, pinned and cemented to turned ivory bases, which for the bishops, knights, and pawns are in two parts assembled by threading. The bases for the dark side are dyed red. H: king 4^1/s inches, pawn 1^5/s inches.   48.174.129a–p, aa–pp

The two kings resemble Kaiser Wilhelm of Germany and Czar Alexander III of Russia, and resemblances to the Empress Augusta and Czarina Maria Feodorovna may be intended in the queens. The reigns of the Kaiser and Alexander III overlapped from 1887 to 1894. This period may thus be taken as the probable time in which the set was made. The initials J s in monogram within a shaped shield on the four rooks are probably those of the original owner.

Russian P, R, KT, B, Q, K

Admiral Alfred von Tirpitz, Field Marshal Kurt von Mackensen, General Enver Pasha, Field Marshal Paul von Hindenburg, Field Marshal Erich Ludendorff, General Felix von Bothmer, General Eduard von Böhm-Ermolli, General Geodorff

53   The First World War   32 chessmen, buff v. black

German, made by Max Niemeier, about 1917–1918. Pearwood or ebony busts carved in one with their turned pedestals. H: king 3⅜ inches, pawn 3¾ inches.

48.174.169a–p, aa–pp

Baron Sidney Sonnino, King Alexander III of Serbia, President Woodrow Wilson, Prime Minister Aristide Briand, Queen Maria of Rumania, Prime Minister David Lloyd George, General Nicolas Nicolaievitch, Prime Minister Eleutherios Venizelos

German marine infantry, Austrian guards (Kaiserjager?), Landwehr, Imperial German navy, Bulgarian infantry, German infantry, Tyrolean Standschütze, Turkish infantry

The pieces on the buff side are portraits of the military leaders on the German side in the first World War; the black side represents the opposing Allied leaders. The pawns are fighting men in various uniforms. The set was evidently made after the entry of America into the war in 1917. Max Nicolaus Niemeier (born 1876) was a portraitist of the German school. A board of inlaid wood is *en suite* with the set.

Serbian, Indian Sikh, French Colonial?, Italian bersagliere, Rumanian, Portuguese, Russian, French Colonial (Senegal)

Hungarian, made by Hurbán of Kolosvar, about 1928. Carved wood figures rising from bases with three feet cemented on, painted in thick oil paint, buff and black with polychrome details. H: king 4³/₄ inches, pawn 2⁵/₈ inches.

48.174.144a–p, aa–pp

The white side represents the Hungarian homeland and the opposition of Hungarian patriots to the Treaty of Trianon, signed on June 4, 1920, at Versailles, between the Allies and the Central Powers. The black side represents the treaty itself. All the pieces except the queens are inscribed, as follows:

White king: MAGYAR HON (the Hungarian homeland)

  bishops: NEM NEM SOHA (no, no, never)

  knights: ERDELYT? SOHA, SOHA (Transylvania? no, never); ERDELYT NEM ADJUK SOHA (Transylvania we never surrender)

  rooks: POZSONY, TEMESVAR, SZABADKA, NAGYVA'RAD; ARAD, KASSA, ZOMBOR, KOLOSVA'R (names of towns situated within the Hungarian borders before the Treaty)

  pawns, peasants kneeling and bound: LUGOS, ESZEK, MUNKACS, EPERJES, TORDA, DEVA, DES, ZILAH (names of towns situated within the Hungarian borders before the Treaty)

Black king, bishops, rooks, and pawns: TRIANON

  knights: TRIANON BEKEJE FEKETE (the peace of Trianon is black); TRIANON BEKEJE GYATZ (the peace of Trianon means mourning)

The bases of all the pieces are slightly domed and shaped to suggest the pre-Trianon boundaries of Hungary. The domed shape also suggests the mountainous central region. On the underside of each piece is an outline map of post-Trianon Hungary painted in the Hungarian colors of red, white, and green.

The Treaty of Trianon was the formal peace treaty between Hungary and the victorious powers at the end of the first World War, against whom Hungary, as part of the Austro-Hungarian Empire, had been at war. Called "the last and most ill-advised" of the peace treaties by Lord Rothermere, it

reduced Hungary from a population of twenty million to eight million, and an area of 125,000 square miles to 36,000 square miles, large areas of land being awarded to her neighbors, Czechoslovakia, Rumania, Yugoslavia, and Austria. Although the Hungarians had no choice but to sign this treaty, her citizens never accepted it as final, and *"Nem, nem, soha,"* which is inscribed on the white bishops of this set, was a slogan of the whole country.

Lord Rothermere, in an editorial in the *London Daily Mail* (which he owned), called for a revision of the Treaty on June 21, 1927. Thereafter he was strongly identified with this cause and received so many handmade gifts from Hungarian patriots that he had to set aside one room in his house to keep them. This set was one of these gifts and was later given by Lord Rothermere to Nandor Fodor, who brought it to New York in about 1941. Dr. Fodor was Lord Rothermere's Hungarian political adviser.

White R, KT, B, K, Q, P

55　The Italo-Ethiopian War　　32 chessmen, white v. brown

Italian, made by Paola Wahl Cortesi, 1937. Pinkish-brown pottery, formed in a mold and hand-finished, partially glazed in white, brown, and black. H: king 4$^1/_2$ inches, pawn 1$^1/_8$ inches.　　　　　　　　　　　　　　53.71.88a–p, aa–pp

The pieces, representing the two sides in the Italian invasion of Ethiopia in 1935–1936, were identified by the maker. The Italian king is Benito Mussolini, the queen Rome. The bishops are Italian standards. Marshal Pietro Badoglio and General Rodolfo Graziani are the knights. Rooks are armored tanks, and the pawns are infantrymen, wearing black shirts. For the Ethiopian side, the king is the Emperor Haile Selassie, the queen the Empress Manin. Bishops are again standards, and the knights are Ras Desta Demtu, the son-in-law of the Emperor, and General Tecle Hawariate. The Ethiopian rooks are huts, and pawns are barefoot spear-throwers. A pottery board is *en suite*, with black and white glazed squares, mounted on wood. For another version of this subject, see Hammond, *The Book of Chessmen*, pl. XLVII.

TOP: Italian R, B, KT, K, Q, P.　　BOTTOM: Ethiopian R, B, KT, K, Q, P

56 32 chessmen, silver v. gold

German, late XVIII century. Cast silver, soldered to thin disklike bases. The pieces for the dark side are gilded. H: king 3 inches, pawn 2 inches.   48.174.73a–p, aa-pp

The pieces and the board they came with were probably made by Friederich Donaleitis of Königsberg in 1778 from a seventeenth-century prototype. The bases are boldly engraved with numbers from 1 to 32 on the underside. It has been thought that the set represents the Battle of Panormus (present-day Palermo), fought in 250 B.C. between the Romans under Metellus and the Carthaginians under Hasdrubal, but this is hypothetical. The subject of Romans and Barbarians was a popular one in all forms of art.

The silver king and queen each carry a scepter. The bishops are standard-bearers, as was common in Europe, probably because of the corruption of the Arabic *al fil* (the elephant) into the Italian *alfiere* (standard-bearer). The knights are horsemen with swords, and the rooks are elephants with castles on their backs, a form that M. A. H. Vida introduced in his sixteenth-century poem on chess, and which proved popular. The pawns are Roman soldiers, six with spears, two with swords. On the opposing side the king and queen have tall conical hats and hold orbs and scepters. The bishops are standard-bearers. The knights, without weapons, ride a very peculiar form of animal that is meant to be a camel, but has horse's hooves and no hump—not uncommon errors in European attempts to depict the camel. The rooks are like those on the silver side, except that the castles are furnished with conical tops. The pawns, in various headdresses, carry bows and arrows.

A set based on similar prototypes, with ivory figures versus wooden ones, is in the Bavarian National Museum, Munich, and has been ascribed to the end of the sixteenth century, which seems a little early. Another, in the Hesse State Museum in Kassel, is given a dating of the latter part of the seventeenth century.

Back: Barbarian P, Roman KT, Barbarian B; front: Roman R, K

57   Romans and Germans   32 chessmen, silver v. gold

German, about 1860. Cast silver, soldered to hollow octagonal bases. The pieces for the dark side are gilded. H: king 3 inches, pawn 2¼ inches.

48.174.47a–p, aa–pp

The pawns hold shields with heraldic arms on them indicating the opposing parties, but they do not appear to be valid. The set probably represents Rome against German tribes, but in a German style that has prototypes for the kings and knights in the seventeenth century. Here the figures have become wooden and lack all subtlety in modeling. Such cast sets, however, were popular in the so-called "Historical Period," around 1860. A board of unpainted sycamore and ebonized wood squares set in a frame with a gilt-bronze gallery on short legs is *en suite* with the set.

TOP: Roman P, R, KT, B, Q, K.   BOTTOM: German P, R, KT, B, Q, K

58   Christians and Muslims   32 chessmen

Russian, second half of the XVIII century. Walrus ivory, carved figures on carved and pierced bases, cemented to second bases, which are carved, pierced, and undercut. H: king $3^{1}/_{2}$ inches, pawn $2^{1}/_{4}$ inches.   60.146a–p, aa–pp

The standard opposition between Christianity and Islam is here depicted as an opposition of recognizably Roman soldiers and turbaned, long-robed Turks, that is, the struggle of the Byzantine Empire against the Ottoman Turks, which culminated in the fall of Constantinople in 1453. Although the Roman pawns and knights seem to be modeled on German originals, other aspects of the set recall the earlier Indian conventions. Russia developed much trade with India during the reign of Ivan the Terrible (1544–1584), who liked chess and died while playing the game. There is a general in place of the queen, and elephants instead of bishops. These have a rider on the "good" side and are riderless on the "bad" side (see also Nos. 22 and 59). The use of ships for rooks reflects the Indian custom that was adopted in Bengal in the seventeenth or eighteenth century, where the Persian *rukh* was confused with the Sanskrit *roka* (ship). The knights are on rearing horses with both forelegs high off the ground, a peculiarity in Germany and elsewhere in Europe in the seventeenth and eighteenth centuries. The kings wear typical eighteenth-century queues, and although they sit with feet crossed one over the other, Byzantine style, they have chairs with eighteenth-century backs. Thus the set combines details from many places, including India, Germany, and Byzantium, and yet is unmistakably Russian.

Christian R, KT, B, Q, K, P

59 Christians and Turks   32 chessmen, white v. red

Russian, XVIII–XIX century. Carved walrus ivory figures on octagonal reel-shaped bases; the pieces for the dark side are dyed red. H: king 3 inches, pawn 1⁷/₈ inches.
48.174.123a–p, aa–pp

Eastern convention is followed in having a general instead of a queen, and an elephant instead of a bishop—with a rider for the "good" side, without for the "bad" side. Russian convention has ships for rooks; here they too are differentiated, by being double-masted on the "good" side, having only one mast on the other. The white king, general, and pawns are dressed like Roman soldiers, the corresponding red pieces like Turks. The white king and general have European mid-eighteenth-century hairstyles, with long curls above the ears and long queues tied with a ribbon at the neck. This set is thus very characteristic of a group of Russian sets in which some Eastern conventions are seen alongside of European ones (see also No. 58).

Turkish R, KT, B, K, Q, P

60   Crusaders and Muslims   32 chessmen, silver v. gold

German (Hanau), probably 1845–1860. Cast iron, pewtered or gilded. H: king 2³/₄ inches, pawn 1³/₈ inches.   48.174.172a–p, aa–pp

The Crusaders are the pewtered side. Their king has a cross on his tunic and is in medieval armor; the bishops and pawns are in helmets of early seventeenth-century style. The Muslims are the gilded side; their pedestals are slightly different from those of the other side.

The E. G. Zimmerman Company of Hanau, who probably made the set, was one of the firms specializing in small cast-iron productions such as chess sets. On the underside of each piece is scratched the word "Germany," perhaps in accordance with the McKinley Tariff Act of 1897, which would indicate that the set was imported after that date.

Crusader R, KT, B, K, Q, P

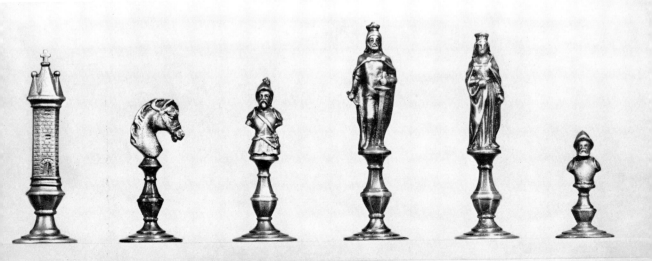

61   Crusaders and Muslims   32 chessmen, white v. black

French, about 1929. Hard-paste porcelain cast in a mold in one piece, with polychrome enamels and gilding. H: king 4¹/₂ inches, pawn 3 inches.

48.174.99a–p, aa–pp

The set has been supposed to represent the Battle of Mansura in Egypt, which took place in 1249 during the Seventh Crusade, led by St. Louis (Louis IX, reigned 1226–1270). In this battle Louis was defeated by Beibars the Mameluke, who later ruled Egypt and Syria. There is nothing to identify the set especially with this battle, and it must be considered as one of many examples with Crusaders versus Muslims as the subject.

"Roby, Paris, Made in France" is marked on all the bases.

TOP: Crusader R, KT, B, K, Q, P.   BOTTOM: Muslim R, KT, B, K, Q, P

62 Europeans and Africans   32 chessmen, white v. black

French, about 1870–1880. Carved ivory busts, painted black for the Moorish side, cemented to turned ivory or ebony stands made in two pieces threaded together. Rooks and pawns are single pieces of turned ivory or ebony. H: king 3¹/₂ inches, pawn 2 inches.   48.174.153a–p, aa–pp

The shapes of the pieces are identical on the two sides, except for the kings and queens. The workmanship of the rooks and pawns is especially fine. The bishops, as is customary in French sets, are *fous,* wearing jester's cap and belled collar. The white king may be meant to represent King Ferdinand of Spain, which would support the theory that this set represents the reconquest of Spain from the Moors, and was intended for the Spanish market.

TOP: European R, KT, B, K, Q, P.   BOTTOM: African R, KT, B, K, Q, P

63   Christians and Barbarians   32 chessmen, buff v. black

Austrian, second half of the XIX century. Carved fir, painted black for the dark side. H: king 4 inches, pawn 2³/₄ inches.   48.174.26a–p, aa–pp

Whereas the kings appear to illustrate the standard theme of Christians against Turks, which is carried through in the Hungarian-inspired military attire of the bishops, knights, and pawns on the buff side, the remaining figures on the black side are strongly suggestive, with their bows and arrows, feather skirts, and headdresses, of the European idea of "barbarians" rather than simple Muslims. This dichotomy is to be seen in a silver set of an earlier century (No. 56). These vivid little figures, though products of the nineteenth century, probably derive from eighteenth-century prototypes, which in turn would certainly have owed something to the personifications of Africa and America current since the sixteenth century (see C. Le Corbeiller, "Miss America and Her Sisters," *The Metropolitan Museum of Art Bulletin*, XIX [1961], 209).

LEFT: Christian K, Q, B, KT, R, P.   RIGHT: Barbarian K, Q, B, KT, R, P

64   French and Africans   32 chessmen, white v. red

African (French Colonial?), late XVIII–early XIX century. Carved bone busts drilled and cemented to plugs on turned baluster stands. The rooks are turned work in two parts joined by threading. The pieces for the dark side are dyed red. H: rook 3¹/₂ inches, pawn 2¹/₄ inches.   48.174.142a–p, aa–pp

The same general facial characteristics appear on the white king, queen, and *fou,* and—most consistently—on the pawns, who are said to represent the Chevalier de Boufflers (1736–1815), governor of Senegal from 1785 to 1788. The animal heads of the knights resemble camels rather than horses and have half-figures riding as though at the base of the curving neck. The other principal pieces are similar on the two sides, except for the earrings and cropped hair on the African side. The rooks are incised and cut to suggest brickwork and crenelations. They and the stands are possibly of French manufacture, added to imported carved pieces made to order from a French model.

TOP: French P, R, KT, B, Q, K.   BOTTOM: African P, R, KT, B, Q, K

65   Christians and Muslims   32 chessmen, dark v. light brown

Austrian (Tyrol), late XIX century. Carved wood figures on rounded bases cemented to turned, reel-shaped stands. The Christians are of birch with yew bases; the Muslims are of spindle wood. H: king 4¹/₈ inches, pawn 2⁷/₈ inches.

48.174.50a–p, aa–pp

The classic opposition of Christian and Muslim seems here to be presented as an opposition between Tyroleans and one of the Muslim peoples within the Austro-Hungarian Empire (possibly in an area of modern Yugoslavia, such as Bosnia-Herzegovina). The dress of the queens is clearly modeled on the styles of the period 1828 to 1835, but the pieces are undoubtedly of later date. The king of the Christian side bears a strong resemblance to the Emperor Franz Josef and may be taken from a youthful portrait of him. The Muslims are the light side.

Christian R, KT, B, K, Q, P

66   Good and Evil   32 chessmen, white v. red

Bohemian(?), late XIX century. Carved ivory figures on irregular domed bases cemented to turned ivory disks. The red pieces were dyed after assembly. H: king 4¼ inches, pawn 2½ inches.   48.174.35a–p, aa–pp

The white side seems to represent the principle of Good, the red the powers of Darkness. The figure of the red king is closely modeled on a familiar prototype of Mephistopheles. Liddell illustrates a very similar set, probably from the same workshop, which is attributed, without any foundation, to Florence (*Chessmen*, 11th ill. after p. 82).

TOP: "Good" R, KT, B, K, Q, P.   BOTTOM: "Evil" R, KT, B, K, Q, P

67 Communists and Capitalists   32 chessmen, red v. black

Russian, about 1928. Hard-paste porcelain cast in a mold in one piece, with gilding and colored enamels: orange, pink, rose, and maroon for the Communist side, and black, gray, and brown for the capitalists. H: king 4¼ inches, pawn 2⅜ inches.

48.174.40a–p, aa–pp

The pieces are highly propagandistic in treatment in favor of Communism. The king on the capitalist side is represented as Death in armor and an ermine-lined cloak, and the queen as Fortuna with a cornucopia, from which, however, not produce, but gold coins, are spilling out. The pawns are in chains. On the Communist side the king is an honest blacksmith, and the queen has a true horn of plenty. The pawns hold sickles and sheaves of wheat. Following the Russian chess tradition, inherited from czarist days, the rooks are boats (see Nos. 58 and 59). Other sets with the same subject matter have been made in painted wood, with the capitalist king as a financier in a top hat (Liddell, *Chessmen*, opp. p. 62).

All the pieces are marked on the underside with a hammer and sickle and "Made in Russia, U.S.S.R." in red enamel. They were made at the State Porcelain Manufactory near Leningrad, which was formerly the Imperial Porcelain Factory, St. Petersburg. The interest in making chess sets of porcelain survives even major political changes—just as does the game itself.

TOP: Communist R, KT, B, K, Q, P.   BOTTOM: Capitalist R, KT, B, K, Q, P

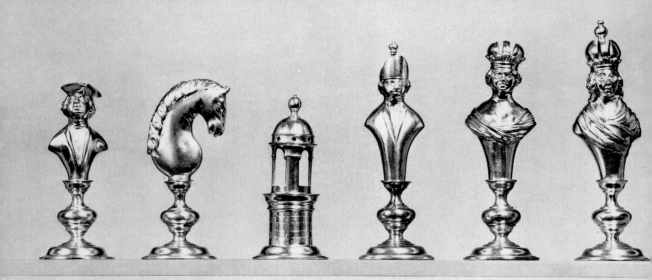

68 32 chessmen, silver v. gold

Austrian (Vienna), 1767. Cast silver half-figures threaded to cast and polished baluster stands. The dark side is gilded. H: king 3¾ inches, pawn 2¾ inches.

48.174.90a–p, aa–pp

The pieces of the two sides are similar. The kings and queens wear the divided Austrian crown; the bishops are soldiers wearing the regulation hat for the Austrian infantry introduced in 1767; the pawns wear the tricorne hat, which continued to be worn by the Austrian artillery after 1767. The kings and queens may be portraits of Maria Theresa and Josef II of Austria. The bases bear the Vienna hallmark for 1767 and the mark of the silversmith, I C B. A board of silver and silver-gilt squares set in a wooden frame on four legs is *en suite* with this set.

P, KT, R, B, Q, K

69   32 chessmen, silver v. gold

German, about 1840–1850. Cast silver figures on high round bases soldered to hollow stands. H: king 4 inches, pawn 2 9/16 inches.   48.174.2a–p, aa–pp

The costume of the principal figures appears to be a romantic version of medieval dress; certain features, however, of the dress of the queen are unmistakably of the decade 1840 to 1850, thus dating the entire set. A board of white and black mother-of-pearl squares set in a silver-plated metal frame is *en suite.*

P, R, KT, B, Q, K

70 32 chessmen

South German (Nuremberg?), second half of the XIX century. Wood, carved figures on rounded bases cemented to turned reel-shaped bases in two parts also cemented together. The figures of one side are of maple, those of the other, and all of the bases, are of pear wood, all now darkened to a uniform brown. H: rook 5 inches, pawn 3½ inches.   48.174.80a–p, aa–pp

The figure of the king, with his large beard and battle-axe, seems to be a representation of an early German hero-king. The pawns are countrymen.

K, Q, B, KT, R, P

71   Blondes and Brunettes   32 chessmen, blonde v. brunette

German, about 1830–1840. Hard-paste porcelain, painted with enamels and gilding.
H: king 2¹/₂ inches, pawn 2¹/₈ inches.   48.174.5a–p, aa–pp

The sides are distinguished by the hair color of the figures, blonde or brunette, and the bases, which are enameled on the blonde side, left white on the brunette side. The set is quite practical, and apart from the subject of its opposition is rather conventional in its major pieces. The king, queen, knight, and rook are in no way unusual; the bishops, however, are ladies, which is not customary. The set was made at the Royal Berlin Porcelain Factory.

Blonde P, B, brunette Q, K, KT, blonde R

72   32 chessmen, silver v. black

German, early XIX century. Cast silver figures on domed bases, soldered to hollow cylindrical plinths with flat octagonal bases. The pieces of one side are polished, those of the other are oxidized. H: king $3^{1}/_{4}$ inches, pawn $2^{1}/_{4}$ inches.

48.174.34a–p, aa–pp

A somewhat baffling combination of pieces: both sides have as king St. George killing the dragon, but without a saddle or reins; as queen a mounted barbarian with a bearskin instead of a saddle and carrying a spear. Bishops are griffins with their right claws resting on a miter. The silver knights are mounted figures in armor, carrying lances; black knights are foot soldiers in armor, with the cross of St. George on their shields and breastplates. The silver rooks are camels, and the black rooks are rhinoceroses, both with towers on their backs. Running stags are the silver pawns, and the black pawns are bears at bay. The figures are probably south German, with stands possibly added in England. There are no hallmarks on the silver.

The set is said to have been given by George III to one of his physicians, Dr. Tyler, and the shape of the stands is explained as that of pillboxes. Early nineteenth-century pillboxes, however, were not of this form; and although the unusual elongation of the box that came with the pieces (impressed with royal crowns and GR) suggests that it may have once been a case for medical instruments, thus confirming *its* connection with Dr. Tyler, there is no evidence that the chessmen have always belonged with the box. The set, rather, seems to be made up from two different sets, one with hunting figures and one with military figures, possibly from the same workshop, which would account for their similarity in scale. The use of tall bases is not peculiar, apart from the form, to this set, for other nineteenth-century sets show that such were fashionable, usually in the shape of truncated columns (see Hammond, *The Book of Chessmen*, pl. LIV). The introduction of camels and rhinoceroses seems to reflect hybrid ideas resulting from certain Indian sets made for the foreign market (see No. 11).

REFERENCE: Liddell, *Chessmen*, 6th ill. after p. 42.

Silver K, black R, silver P, B

73 Threshers and Mowers   29 chessmen, white v. black

Austrian, about 1820. Carved ivory figures on small irregular bases pegged and cemented to turned ivory or horn stands made in two sections joined by threading. H: king 4 inches, pawn 3 inches.   48.174.157a–e, g–o, aa–ee, gg–pp

The stands, hats, and crowns of the figures on the mowers' (black) side are of a naturally dark horn. There are also faint traces of an orange-brown stain on some of the pieces of the dark side, and all the figures have traces of red paint for the lips. This charming set was originally, therefore, much more colorful than it is now. It is one of those sets in which the theme of the opposition is seen in the pawns rather than the principal pieces, which are identical on the two sides. Both kings wear the divided Austrian crown. The bishops are couriers, and the rearing horses for the knights are fully modeled but riderless. The rooks are towers with very large bell-shaped finials. Pawns, peasants, on the white side are threshers with flails, on the dark side mowers with scythes. A white pawn and bishop and a black bishop are missing.

Back: black R, K; front: black KT, white P, black B, white Q

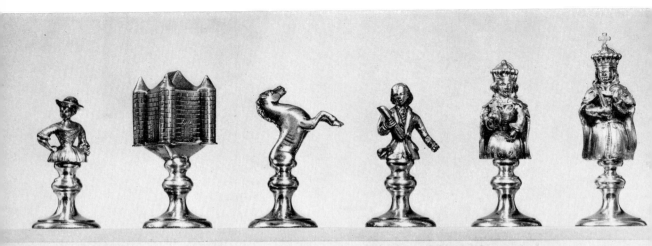

74   The Battle of the Sexes   32 chessmen, silver v. gold

Austrian (Vienna?), about 1850–1860. Cast silver, half-figures soldered to baluster stands, gilded for the dark side. H: king 3³/₄ inches, pawn 2¹/₂ inches.

48.174.136a–p, aa–pp

The principal pieces are similar on each side, with poets carrying scrolls for bishops. The knights are horses that emerge at the haunches with forelegs raised in a prancing attitude. The castles seem disproportionately large to the rest of the major pieces. Pawns are peasant girls on the silver side, and young men on the gold side. The bases are marked "13–1783," the Viennese silver warranty mark for 1783. The mark applies to the bases only; the figural parts are of the nineteenth century.

Silver P, R, KT, B, Q, K

75   32 chessmen, white v. black

Czechoslovakian, about 1920–1940. Wood, turned, except the knight, which is a cutout; the major pieces cemented to turned wood bases. Painted in oil, white or black with polychrome details. H: king 2⁷/₈ inches, pawn 1¹/₈ inches.

53.71.17a–p, aa–pp

The pieces of turned wood form stylized anthropomorphic shapes, in peasant dress, with the exception of the rook, which is a tower.

Black P, R, KT, B, Q, K

76   32 chessmen, white v. foxy red

North Labradorian, xx century. Walrus ivory, stained foxy-red for the dark side, with some painted details. H: king 2 1/16 inches, pawn 1⁵/₈ inches.

53.71.28a–p, aa–pp

The king and queen are an Eskimo man and woman, the latter wearing a tailed parka (essentially a woman's garment) and no head covering. Her short round haircut is typically Eskimo. The bishops are probably white men in long parkas, possibly meant to be surplices. There are dog heads for knights, igloos for rooks, and harpoon steels for pawns. The pieces have pegs rather than bases, and fit into holes on the board. The mahogany box hinges open at the top and front to give access to the board of walrus ivory and mahogany squares, fixed to the bottom. This set was probably made in Hebron, Ramah, or Kidlinik and sold through the Moravian Brethren Mission at Nain, Labrador, where it was probably acquired by the International Grenfell Association.

R, KT, B, Q, K, P

77   32 chessmen, white v. red

Lapland, about 1925. Mammoth ivory, carved figures cemented to turned bases. The rooks are single pieces of ivory. The bases of one side are painted red (the paint is now much worn). H: king 2¹/₂ inches, pawn 1⁵/₈ inches.

48.174.28a–p, aa–pp

The king is a Laplander holding a pipe, the queen a standing woman. Knights are reindeer heads, and bishops are hunters with rifles. Skin teepees, which resemble very much those of the American Indians, are rooks, and Husky dogs are the pawns. The pieces are identical on both sides.

REFERENCE: Liddell, *Chessmen*, p. 22, ill. opp. p. 35.

P, R, KT, B, K, Q

78 Figures from Shakespeare   32 chessmen, lilac v. gray

English, XIX century, after a design by John Flaxman of 1783. Jasper ware, cast in one piece with their reel-shaped bases. H: king 4 inches, pawn 2 inches.

48.174.130a–p, aa–pp

The designs after which the set was modeled were made by John Flaxman for Josiah Wedgwood. The kings represent Charles Kemble as Macbeth, the queens Mrs. Siddons as Lady Macbeth and the Tragic Muse. Among the pawns are three figures of jesters, made to replace bishops in sets to be sold in France. All four knights are the same but for the color.

There are many variations of the original set designed by Flaxman, some are in the British Museum and the Soane Museum, London (K. Mathews, *British Chess*, London, 1948, opp. p. 42). The bases vary, including rough mounds, wooden ones, and reel shapes. The design is bold in conception and exquisite in execution, making this one of the outstanding sets in the medium. Other ceramic sets were made in England, in blue and white, at Castleford, but they lack the touch of the master designer Flaxman or the grace of the Meissen designs (see Nos. 84 and 104).

REFERENCE: J. D. Holmes and H. H. Cottrell, "The Wedgwood Chessmen," *The Antique Collector*, IV (1933), 472–476, 537, 538, 587, 588; V (1934), 12, 13.

Lilac KT, K, Q

79   Alice in Wonderland   32 chessmen, white v. tan

American, made by Sorcha Boru, 1932. Modeled figures on round domed bases. The light pieces are pipe clay, the dark are terracotta. H: king 5⅝ inches, pawn 2¾ inches.   48.174.59a–p, aa–pp

The designs are taken from Sir John Tenniel's illustrations of 1866–1870 for *Alice's Wonderful Adventures in Wonderland* and *Through the Looking-Glass* by Lewis Carroll.

White king: the White Rabbit
  queen: Alice
  bishops: the Mad Hatter and the March Hare
  knights: the White Knight and the Red Knight
  rooks: the Mouse Juror and a Parrot Juror
  pawns: Father William, the Cook, the Mock Turtle, Humpty-Dumpty, the
    Dormouse, the Dodo, the Lion, and the Unicorn

Tan king: the King of Hearts
  queen: the Queen of Hearts
  bishops: the Walrus and the Carpenter
  knights: Tweedledum and Tweedledee
  rooks: the Guinea-pig Juror and a Parrot Juror
  pawns: the Gryphon, the Blue Caterpillar, the Youth, the Frog Footman,
    the Cheshire Cat, the Duchess, the Messenger, and the Knave of Hearts

The pieces are housed in two wooden boxes, one painted on the lid with the Cheshire Cat, the other with the inscription "Curioser and curioser cried Alice."

Other books have been used as subject matter for chess sets, as for example Caxton's *Game and Pley of the Chesse*. Such sets are never of contemporary books, and although books such as Caxton's may have had some influence on the form of particular chessmen, the direct representation of characters from literature was not made before the eighteenth century (see No. 78).

Sorcha Boru was one of the artists who worked in the studios of the Allied Arts Guild, in Menlo Park, California, which also acted as a sales agent, and is still in operation. See also Nos. 81 and 82.

TOP: white K, Q, B, KT, R, P.   BOTTOM: tan K, Q, B, KT, R, P

80 The Discovery of America 32 chessmen, white v. black

Bohemian?, about 1895. Carved ivory figures, some cemented to low turned disk-like bases, the smaller ones rising directly from a turned lower edge. H: king 5¹/₂ inches, pawn 3¹/₄ inches. 48.174.149a–p, aa–pp

Spanish (white) king: Ferdinand I of Spain
   queen: Isabella, queen of Spain
   bishops: Christopher Columbus (in chains) and (possibly) Cortes
   knights: a Catholic bishop and a conquistador
   rooks: ship's prow and stern, with the arms of France and Castile-León on
      the sectioned faces
   pawns: Spanish mariners, soldiers, and colonists

Indian (black) king: an Indian king
   queen: Indian queen
   bishops: Indian warriors
   knights: a scout riding a llama and an archer riding an ostrich
   rooks: medicine men
   pawns: Indian men and women

LEFT: Spanish R, KT, B, K, Q, P.   RIGHT: Indian R, KT, B, K, Q, P

81 The Battle of Saratoga   32 chessmen, silver v. gold

American, made by Parker L. Hall, 1933. Carved magnolia wood, painted in oil, blue or red with polychrome details. The leaf decoration around the bases is silvered on the Colonists' side, gilded on the British side. H: queen 6³/₄ inches, rook 4 inches.

48.174.134a–p, aa–pp

The figures are identified as follows, on typed stickers under the bases:
Colonists' king: Washington
   queen: Liberty
   bishops: General Morgan; General Gates
   knights (flags): Cambridge Jan. 2, 1776 Flag; Continental Congress June
      14th 1777
   pawns (two of each): Penn Line Infantry; N.Y. Line Infantry; Continental
      Artillery; Morgan Riflemen
British king: King George III
   queen: Britannia
   bishops: General Burgoyne; General Fraser
   knights (flags): British Colonial; Great Britain, adopted 1707
   pawns (two of each): Iroquois Indian; British Grenadier; Dragoon Private
      (Brunswick); Canadian Militia
The rooks are military drums supporting scroll maps, representing the phases of the battle. The Colonists' maps are inscribed *I, Sept. 19 1777* and *Surrender of British, Oct. 17 1777.* The British maps have the inscriptions *II Oct 7 1777* and *III Oct 8 1777.*

The set and the following one were designed and made by Parker Hall, in the studios of the Allied Arts Guild of California, Menlo Park, California.

Back: Colonist Q, British P, P, KT; front: Colonist KT, P, British K, Colonist K

82 The Conversion of California   32 chessmen, silver v. gold

American, made by Parker L. Hall, 1932. Carved magnolia wood, with polychrome oil paint. The bases are silvered or gilt. H: king 5 inches, pawn 3 inches.

53.71.86a–p, aa–pp

The silver king and queen are Charles III of Spain and his wife Maria Amelia of Saxony; the silver bishops are Franciscan friars. The heraldic device of León is painted on the shields of the knights. Rooks are mission churches, and the pawns are converted Indians. The gold king and queen are a Californian Indian chief and woman; the bishops are Indian men, the knights pumas, rooks are teepees, and the pawns are unconverted Indians. The set illustrates the Mission Period (1769–1823), when California was a colony of Spain, during which the missions of Dominicans in lower California and of Franciscans in upper California controlled the resources of the colony and the obedience of the Indians. This and the preceding set were made by Parker Hall in the studios of the Allied Arts Guild, Menlo Park, California. See also No. 79.

TOP: Indian R, KT, B, K, Q, P.   BOTTOM: Spanish R, KT, B, K, Q, P

83 Cowboys and Indians   32 chessmen

American, made by Robert Leach, about 1930. Carved sweet-gum wood, made in one piece with their bases, painted in red, blue, brown, and green. H: king 4³/₄ inches, pawn 1¹/₂ inches.   48.174.139a–p, aa–pp

The set is one of many that illustrate domestic incidents in national history. The subject, presumably the contest between American Indians and American whites, shows a number of inconsistencies. For example, no such white "cowboy" types fought in such lookouts against American Indians. The crude workmanship and the naiveté displayed here make a set like this the opposite of European nineteenth-century "historical" sets, with their careful revival of past ages. Each piece has the engraved signature LEACH on the base.

TOP: Cowboy K, Q, B, KT, R, P.   BOTTOM: Indian K, Q, B, KT, R, P

84 32 chessmen, white v. red

German, XIX century. Hard-paste porcelain cast in a mold, with polychrome enamels and gilding. H: king 2^1/$_8$ inches, pawn 1 15/16 inches.　　　53.71.27a–p, aa–pp

The pieces are mainly of nineteenth-century Meissen manufacture, though there are some replacements of nineteenth-century Berlin manufacture and some of more recent date. All the pieces derive in their design from an eighteenth-century Meissen original. The set reflects a certain spirit of the eighteenth century, for it emphasizes a frivolous aspect of the "Age of Reason." The rather affected adjustment of hats is to be seen in other sets, some of ivory. In the latter the hats are sometimes made of leather and are removable. Although there is a touch of cuteness in such sets, they are nonetheless charming.

As shown, the pieces reconstruct a game between the master H. E. Bird and an amateur in London in 1886. The game is shown at the point just before the eleventh move. Bird, playing white, effected a checkmate on the thirteenth.

85 32 chessmen, white v. black

Polish, xx century. Carved poplar, painted in oil, white or black with polychrome details. H: king 5 inches, pawn 3¹/₄ inches.   53.71.90a–p, aa–pp

The figures wear Polish dress of the Carpathian region. The white side wears the dress of the Szczawnica area, the black side that of the Spitz area. The axes carried by the kings may indicate some specific local contest, perhaps be-tween woodsmen of rival villages. There are anachronistic elements in some of these modern peasant sets, the spirit being that of a past century. There is German influence in the bishop being a runner. The rearing horse is a type of knight popular in the eighteenth century.

Back: white KT, B; front: white R, Q, K

86   32 chessmen, silver v. gold

Spanish(?), late XVIII–early XIX century. Cast bronze, polished and engraved, one side silvered. H: king 4¼ inches, pawn 2 inches.   48.174.32a–p, aa–pp

The set was acquired in Barcelona in 1930. The chessmen are an excellent example of a conventional type that rivals that of Staunton (see No. 97), if not indeed being superior to it. It still retains a number of eighteenth-century characteristics in the general shaping and in the bishop, which has merely a slight mark across the top and not a recognizable miter. A set very similar in style to this appears as the engraved frontispiece to *Chess Made Easy* (London, 1797, reproduced in K. Matthews, *British Chess*, London, 1948, p. 35).

R, KT, B, K, Q, P

87 32 chessmen, white v. red

Spanish or French, late XVIII century. Turned and carved ivory and boxwood or ivory and ebony (for the dark side). The ivory sections are assembled with threading, the wood sections with plugs and cement. The ivory on the dark side is dyed red. H: king 3½ inches, pawn 1½ inches. 48.174.30a–p, aa–pp

Modern Mexican sets have preserved some of the features of these chessmen. They often have similar spheres on the stems, divided at the middle with some form of decoration (see No. 108). Lead weights have been inserted in the bases.

R, KT, B, K, Q, P

88   32 chessmen, white v. brown

Portuguese, second half of the XVIII century. Turned, drilled, and carved bone. The pawns and the bases of the principal pieces for the dark side are stained brown. H: king 3⅜ inches, pawn 2¼ inches.   48.174.137a–p, aa–pp

The king, queen, knight, and bishop are busts with almost no shoulders, fixed at the closed base of a circular gallery that extends halfway up their height. The gallery is finished with a row of upright leaves. The rook is a higher gallery narrowing toward the top, ending with a ring of four crenelations and topped by a small central knob. The pawns are half-figures, again with almost no shoulders, fixed to a baluster on a short stand. This type of chessman, with encircling galleries of vertical leaves, has been popular in Spain. The galleries in the simpler sets enclose symbols, miters and conventional substitutions for crowns, rather than busts (Hammond, *The Book of Chessmen*, pl. LI). A set similar to the present one is shown in pl. LII of Hammond; see also p. 69 of that book, and J. F. Harbeson, *Nine Centuries of Chess* (Philadelphia, 1964), no. 150.

The idea of a gallery does not seem to have been popular elsewhere in Europe, where the tendency is to place busts on truncated columns of various shapes, or other pedestals. The peculiar form of pawn appears also in Europe in sets that have been attributed to Yugoslavia. This form also went via the Portuguese to Macao, where the body is transformed into an elaborate balustrade topped by a head (see No. 31).

There is a possibility that this set and some others like it are actually the work of Africans from Sierra Leone or Benin living in Lisbon.

R, KT, B, K, Q, P

89 32 chessmen, gray v. amber

French, late XVIII–early XIX century. Turned boxwood and ivory bodies with turned, pierced, and carved finials of white bone. The wood is varnished, and the ivory dyed with tobacco juice for the dark side. H: king 3¹/₄ inches, pawn 1⁵/₈ inches.

48.174.79a–p, aa–pp

The shapes of the pieces, especially the urn-shaped bodies of the king and queen, are very typical of the second half of the eighteenth century. The shape of the horse heads continued into the beginning of the nineteenth century. A very similar set, of ivory and hornbeam, in the Maunoury Collection, is illustrated in Wichmann, *Chess*, pl. 154, where it is said to be French, of the end of the eighteenth century.

K, Q, B, KT, R, P

90 32 chessmen, silver v. gold

Maltese, first half of the XIX century. Silver or gold filigree. H: king 2³/₈ inches, pawn 1¹/₈ inches.   53.71.51a–p, aa–p

The original board is of rosewood, mounted on four silver feet in the form of hollow spheres; its shagreen case has a brass handle. The set was compact, evidently made for traveling. It was probably for British use; the British were confirmed in the control of the Island of Malta by the Treaty of Paris in 1814, having administered it provisionally since 1799. A rather similar set is illustrated in Hammond, *The Book of Chessmen*, pl. XLV, reputedly made for Madame de Staël.

Left to right: Q, K, P, B, KT

91 32 chessmen, white v. brown

German, first half of the XIX century. Turned, carved, and drilled ivory or ebony, made in several sections and assembled by threading. H: king 4 inches, pawn 1½ inches.   53.71.18a–p, aa–pp

There is a set very similar to this in the German National Museum, Nuremberg, said to have been made in the first half of the nineteenth century (see Wichmann, *Chess*, pl. 161).

R, KT, B, K, Q, P

92 32 chessmen, white v. rose

English, mid-XIX century. Turned and carved bone, made in several sections and assembled by threading. The finials on the kings appear to be ivory. One side is painted deep rose. H: king 3⅝ inches, pawn 1¾ inches.   48.174.15a–p, aa–pp

The set suggests some of the qualities to be seen in the design that was registered as Staunton in 1849 (see No. 97). Although somewhat crude in workmanship, it still embodies some of the elegance and decorative quality that were features of early nineteenth-century pieces.

R, KT, B, K, Q, P

93   27 chessmen, light brown v. black

German (Franconia?), XIX century. Turned and carved boxwood or ebony. H: king 4½ inches, pawn 2 inches.   48.174.31a–d, f–n, aa–dd, ff–oo

The kings with serrated balconies are a refinement of the royal forms to be seen in G. Selenus, *Der Schach, oder König Spiel* (Leipzig, 1616). The knights in that book, however, are addorsed horse heads. A king, a queen, and three pawns are missing. Omitted from the photograph is a bishop, which is very similar in form to that in set No. 91, with the addition of a cross. For a related set, see No. 95.

R, KT, K, Q, P

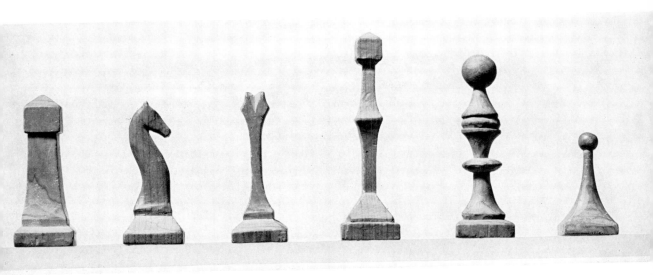

94 30 chessmen, cream v. buff

American, about 1863–1865. Ash or pine, made by whittling. H: king 2¹/₂ inches, pawn 1¹/₄ inches. 48.174.22a–o, aa–oo

According to Stanton family tradition, this set was made by Byron W. Stanton while confined in a Confederate prison during the Civil War. His brother, Edwin Stanton, was Secretary of War in Lincoln's cabinet. The set, despite being made under adverse conditions and not by a professional wood-carver, is distinctive and elegant as well as practical. Not only are famous battles embodied in chess sets, but special situations caused by war, such as imprisonment or the lack of normal recreation, have encouraged the making of sets by soldiers. Sets have also been made by using cartridges or similar material easily come by in circumstances of war (see Nos. 98 and 101).

These pieces are kept in a drum-shaped tobacco box, stamped on the bottom "Patent Package Co/ Newark/ New Jersey/ PAT^D AUG 31 1858" and labeled on the side "Carroll. Lynchburg, Va." One pawn from each side is missing.

R, KT, B, K, Q, P

95 32 chessmen, light v. dark brown

German, about 1885. Turned, drilled, and carved olive wood, made in sections cemented together. The dark side is stained. H: king 3¹/₄ inches, pawn 2 inches.

48.174.16a–p, aa–pp

The glass-topped box has a paper label reading: *"Zur erinnerung an die 3 Schachparthien zwischen Aachen & Leipzig vom 16/11 84 – 9/8 85"* (In memory of the three chess matches between Aachen and Leipzig from November 16, 1884, to August 9, 1885). The winner of the matches was Leipzig. Germany produced a number of these elegantly made chess sets, usually of wood but occasionally of ivory (No. 99). Even more fragile chessmen were made in Denmark. A set in the Danish Museum of Industrial Art has "crow's nests" of lacy forms and twisting stems of triple "threads" (Wichmann, *Chess*, pl. 159). A peculiarity with the knight is the development of two addorsed horse heads, a form that goes back to the early seventeenth century. In some sets there is nothing to indicate that the piece is associated with a horse, and it is distinguished by an incomplete ruff, or a cut aslant. This design occurs as early as the sixteenth century.

R, KT, B, K, Q, P

96 32 chessmen, white v. black

North American (Eskimo), XIX century. Carved walrus ivory or horn, with a few accents in red or black paint. One of the pawns on the dark side is of a lighter kind of horn, made by turning. H: king 2¹/₈ inches, pawn ⁷/₈ inch.

48.174.162a–p, aa–pp

The animals have a whimsical quality—their heads are not truly realistic. The rooks are exceptionally small castles, and the pawns are obviously copied from standard pawns of the nineteenth century.

P, R, KT, B, Q, K

97   32 chessmen, white v. red

French, XIX–XX century. Ivory, turned and carved, in several sections assembled by threading. The colored pieces are dyed red. H: king 2⅞ inches, pawn 1½ inches.

53.71.34a–p, aa–pp

This set is of the design standardized and registered in 1849 with the name of (Howard) Staunton, a Shakespearean actor and scholar. This famous English player brought an end to French superiority in chess by beating Pierre C. F. de Saint-Amant in 1843 in a series of games. It would seem that he judiciously avoided playing against the American prodigy Paul Morphy. There is a leather board *en suite*.

R, KT, B, K, Q, P

98   31 chessmen, white v. red

French, probably 1914–1918. Carved oak finials, painted white or red, fitted to brass cartridges. H: king 3¹/₂ inches, pawn 1¹/₂ inches.   53.71.198a–o, aa–pp

The cartridges are of the type used in the first World War. There seems too little distinction between the kings and queens to warrant this being taken for a "France versus Germany" set. The bishop on each side is represented by a *Pickelhaube*.

REFERENCE: Liddell, *Chessmen*, p. 74 and 10th ill. after p. 74.

R, KT, B, K, Q, P

99 32 chessmen, white v. rose

German, late XVIII–early XIX century. Turned, carved, and drilled ivory made in sections, inset, and cemented. The rose pieces are dyed. H: king 3¹/₂ inches, pawn 2¹/₂ inches. 53.71.100a–p, aa–pp

Gilt-brass beads for handling purposes as well as decoration form finials on the kings, queens, rooks, and pawns. Small ones surmount the balustraded galleries on the knights and rooks. On the four bishops is a gilt-brass tab engraved with the cypher A V I, probably the initials of the set's original owner. This cypher was formerly read as H H, giving rise to the belief that the Berlin Herrenhaus (upper legislative chamber) was its original home (see Liddell, *Chessmen*, p. 82).

White B, P, red KT, K, R

100   32 chessmen, transparent v. cloudy amber

German, XIX century. Amber, turned and cut on the lapidary's wheel. Some chessmen are in two pieces, cemented at a plug-and-socket join. H: king $4^1/_4$ inches, pawn $2^1/_4$ inches.   48.174.72a–p, aa–pp

Each piece has a number from 1 to 32 wheel-engraved on the base, a feature noted in other German sets. The workmanship is typically German, and the horses are well modeled. A box of black morocco leather, with brass mounts and gold tooling, is *en suite;* it opens flat to reveal a hinged board with storage for the chessmen beneath. The set has been attributed to the Hohenzollerns, and although there is no proof for the suggestion, a symbol with words underneath, which would have indicated the original owner, has been obliterated from the box.

    REFERENCE: Liddell, *Chessmen,* opp. p. 91.

Transparent R, P, cloudy P, KT, K

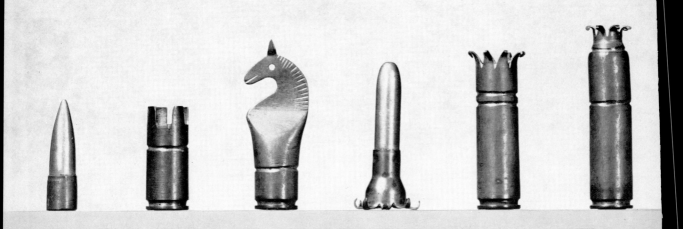

101 32 chessmen, gold v. black

Austrian, 1914–1918. Cartridge cases and bullets. The bases of one side are painted black. H: king 2 inches, pawn 1¹/₈ inches. 48.174.17a–p, aa–pp

The bullets and used cartridge cases are from the first World War. The kings and queens are cartridges with tops opened, cut into points, and turned outward, the queens a little shorter. The bishops are upright bullets, with cases open at the bottom, cut into points, and turned outward. Cartridge cases are flattened at the top and cut in the shape of horse heads for knights, and cut in crenelations at the top for rooks. The bullets for pawns are pointed on one side and rounded on the other. German and Austrian bullets were more pointed than those used by the opposing allies. The use of cartridge cases for making chess sets was not unusual in wartime—cartridges are to hand and are easily adapted. Sometimes the bullets are removed and wooden heads substituted as in set No. 98. This set was bought in Prague in 1936.

P, R, KT, B, Q, K

102   32 chessmen, silver v. black

German, about 1923. Aluminum coins, cut and hammered, assembled with screws and solder. The finials on the queens and bishops are standard copper hardware; the horse's head for the knight is of flattened and cut metal. The black pieces are painted with india ink. H: king 2¹/₈ inches, pawn ³/₄ inch.   48.174.168a–p, aa–pp

The coins are of denominations from 50 pfennigs to 500 marks. Their use as the material for chess pieces is a telling indication of the high degree of inflation in Germany after the first World War. The actual value of the coins was very little; the value of the set was in its workmanship rather than its material. The design is such that the pieces are easily recognizable, and practical for use.

K, Q, B, KT, R, P

103   32 chessmen, brown v. black

German (Weimar), designed by J. Hartwig, 1924. Maple, varnished or painted black, cemented where necessary. H: queen $1^7/8$ inches, pawn $^3/4$ inch.

48.174.64a–p, aa–pp

The sphere, double cube, and three sizes of block, singly or combined, yield pieces that, despite their highly geometric stylization, are strongly suggestive of their rank or power. The bishops are clearly implied by the cross outline, and the rooks by the simple stability of a cube. Most ingenious of all are the knights, formed of three double cubes and a single one joined in such a fashion that three faces of the resulting form show two cubes one above the other and a third on the side, an embodiment of the knight's move.

There have been a number of sets reflecting the new fashions in painting and sculpture started early in the twentieth century. This one was designed by J. Hartwig, one of the designers associated with the Bauhaus movement that flourished in Germany between the wars. It is one of the most imaginative and practical of all such new forms, as well as being attractive in appearance. Such sets were made in other countries, for example, in the U.S.A., one by Man Ray in 1927 (Wichmann, *Chess*, pl. 193a) and one by Oliver Parker (No. 107). A trend in French art is reflected in No. 105.

Black P, K, Q, B, P, white B, R, KT, P

104   32 chessmen, blue v. rose

German, xx century. Hard-paste porcelain, cast in a mold, gilded and enameled. H: king 3⅝ inches, pawn 2 inches.   48.174.97a–p, aa–pp

The finials are crowns for the kings and queens, small military caps for bishops, horse heads for knights, cone-topped towers for rooks, and pointed hats for pawns. Each piece is marked in underglaze blue under the base $\mathscr{F}$ (Fürstenburg porcelain factory, modern mark); in addition, some have CAR/F impressed. This set is a modern example of Fürstenburg porcelain, but probably made from eighteenth-century molds, a procedure followed by this factory especially in the period between the wars. The design was evidently a favorite among porcelain factories, for a set of Meissen porcelain similar to this one, dated about 1755, is in the Bavarian National Museum, Munich; another very similar set, attributed to the English Rockingham porcelain factory and dated about 1823–1826, is shown in Liddell, *Chessmen*, 7th ill. after p. 66.

R, KT, B, K, Q, P

105   32 chessmen, silver v. red

French, probably 1930s. Sheet brass cutouts set in and soldered to low disk-bases, chromium-plated or painted red. H: king 7⅛ inches, pawn 3½ inches.

53.71.175a–p, aa–pp

As is usual in a French set, the bishop is a *fou*. To show his craziness he is standing on his head. The pawns are in the shape of a hand.

R, KT, B, K, Q, P

106 32 chessmen, silver v. gold

Swedish, about 1930. Cast pewter or brass, polished on the wheel. H: king 2 inches, pawn 1¹/₈ inches. 48.174.45a–p, aa–pp

The chessmen are formed of upright, reversed, and truncated cones, in a different combination for each rank. A board of ebony inlaid with disks of polished pewter and brass is *en suite* with the set.

K, Q, B?, KT?, R?, P

107 32 chessmen, silver v. black

American, made by Oliver Parker, about 1934. Black bakelite and polished aluminum pieces assembled by threading. H: king 3 inches, pawn 1³/₈ inches. 48.174.163a–p, aa–pp

Chessmen reflect the use of new metals and other substances, such as bakelite, as well as contemporary styles of decoration. This set, made by Oliver Parker, Long Island, uses standard geometric shapes—cylinder, bead, and disk—in different combinations to produce pieces immediately recognizable to the chess player accustomed to the "conventional" design. It was given to Gustavus A. Pfeiffer by Herman Helms, the publisher of *American Chess Bulletin*, in 1934.

R, KT, B, K, Q, P

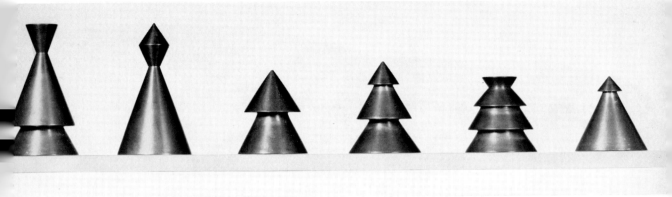

108 32 chessmen, red v. black

Mexican, about 1944. Turned and carved bone finials glued to turned wooden stands painted red or black, with bone beads and lathe-carving. H: king 4¹/₂ inches, pawn 1³/₄ inches.   48.174.25a–p, aa–pp

A Tarascan Indian made this set entirely with a lathe. The employment of this tool, so common in Europe and Asia alike, is unusual among American Indian peoples. For sets such as this the lathe was operated with a bow by one hand; one foot is also used when turning by this method. This form of turning was undoubtedly introduced to Mexico from Spain, where it had been brought as a result of the Arab conquest. An illustration of such a bow lathe in use in an ivory workshop is to be seen in the thirteenth-century book of chess of Alfonso the Wise, in the library of the Escorial, Spain. A bow lathe is also illustrated in H. E. Wulff, *The Traditional Crafts of Persia* (Cambridge, 1966), fig. 133.

R, KT, B, K, Q, P